The Elements of the

Theory of Real Functions

The Elements of the Theory of Real Functions

*Being Notes of Lectures
delivered in the
University of Cambridge*

Third Edition
(Completely revised)

BY

J. E. LITTLEWOOD, F.R.S.

*Fellow of Trinity College, Cambridge,
Late Rouse Ball Professor of Mathematics*

NEW YORK
DOVER PUBLICATIONS, INC.

From the Preface to the Second Edition

THIS book contains the substance of lectures I have given annually for some years at Trinity College. These lectures are intended to introduce third year and the more advanced second year men to the modern theory of functions. The subject-matter is very abstract, but hardly any of it involves genuinely difficult technique. The aim of the lectures, indeed, is to inculcate the proper attitude of enlightened simple-mindedness by concentrating attention on matters which are abstract but not complicated. For this reason, also, I have resisted a constant temptation to introduce new material.

I have aimed at excluding as far as possible anything that could be called philosophy. The average reader, however, is likely to take some interest in the foundations of mathematics; if so, he should certainly study Bertrand Russell's *Introduction to Mathematical Philosophy* in conjunction with the present work.

The subject calls for great precision of statement, and experience has taught me, when lecturing upon it, to dictate word for word all enunciations and proofs. Rather more than half the time has probably been spent in this, the remainder being devoted to explanation and comment of which no record should be necessary. So soon as the lectures ceased to change greatly from year to year it became an obvious course to print the matter formerly dictated, and I carried out the experiment of lecturing from the first edition of printed notes in the Michaelmas term of 1925. The present second edition is slightly enlarged, and is intended to be intelligible independently of the lectures.

I hope, however, that my possible pupils in the University of Cambridge will not too hastily assume that the existence of the notes makes attending the lectures themselves entirely valueless. I am one of those who believe that lectures can have great value, and particularly at a certain moderately advanced stage of a

mathematical education.   The modern standard of conciseness and
lucidity in original papers and advanced text-books is on the whole
a high one, but the style is one for the expert only.   We may demand two things of an original paper, a complete and accurate exposition on the one hand, and on the other that it should convey
what is the real "point" of the subject-matter.   For various reasons,
among which a sufficient one nowadays is sheer lack of space,
the second demand is inevitably sacrificed to the first.   A lecture,
however, more particularly when it is supported by a complete
exposition in print, is the very place for the provisional nonsense
that the second generally calls for.   This would appear ridiculous
if enshrined permanently in print, and its real function is to dis-
appear when it has served its turn.

   I wish, finally, to commend for more general use the practice of
providing lecture notes in advance.   Among obvious advantages
the chief is economy of time and energy: my course formerly con-
sisted of 23 lectures; now, when it is fuller and more discursive,
it consists of 15.   It is possible that the art of lecturing has not
yet recognised the full importance of the younger invention of
printing.

Table of Contents

The Elements of the

Theory of Real Functions

CHAPTER I

Classes and Cardinal Numbers

1. We take for granted all "purely logical" ideas, and pro-, fess to derive all "mathematical" ones from these by definitions. No line can strictly be drawn between mathematics and logic, and we are merely using a more or less popular distinction to indicate our starting point. If we give one selection of "logical" entities and another of "mathematical" ones the reader will probably have a pretty definite idea of where this is.

The following belong to "logic": "true", "proposition", "implies", "not", "and", "or", "there is a ( ) such that", "all", "class", "is a" or "belongs to". We take for granted also the principles of logical inference. One of these is the syllogism, and this may suffice as a specimen. Since most of the important ones have no traditional names the uncritical reader (like Aristotle) uses them without realising that they exist; but what we propose is precisely not to check the actions which are natural to him.

Since a definition is "in terms of" something or other, logic must start by taking some ideas for granted even in the last analysis. It is rather arbitrary precisely which ideas are so taken, but those which are are called "primitive ideas". Similarly a "proof" involves a previously known proposition, and we can start only from propositions known without proof to be true. These (partly arbitrary) initial propositions are called "primitive propositions".

The following belong to "mathematics": "number", "finite", "infinite", "order", "and so on" (in contexts involving the "mathematical induction" with which the reader is in some sense familiar).

We claim, then, that where we do not define our terms they belong to the "logical" class that we take for granted. But the limitations of ordinary language make desirable a certain licence

1

of *expression*. Where there is no definition the essential meaning
is logical, but we hold ourselves free to choose that mode of expression in ordinary language which is most familiar, vivid, or
convenient. For example, the definition in § 3 contains the word
"one", and "one" is strictly a mathematical conception defined
first in § 4. The defence is: (a) we convey to the reader what is
meant; (b) what is meant belongs to "logic"; (c) we could purify
our language if we liked, but the matter is in essence trivial, and
we wish to spare the reader; (d) a systematically purist style is
out of the question. To illustrate the defence we shall for once
give the official meaning. The phrase "every α has exactly one
partner β" means "there is a β which partners α, and if γ partners α then γ is identical with β".

Finally, when we *have* defined a mathematical conception we
hold ourselves free to use, without explicit definition, the language
usually associated with it. Trivial examples are "one" for "1",
"*a* does not exceed *b*" for "it is false that $a > b$"; "set" for
"class" (e.g. "set of classes"); an *important* case occurs in
Chapter II, § 1.

A few special points of "logic" will be the better for special
explanation; they are "=", "ordered pair" ("o.p." for short),
"implies", "function".

"=". In this book the symbol denotes always logical identity,
never a mathematical relation requiring definition; $x = y$ means
that the entity x is identical with the entity y. The reader will
have a useful stand-by if he gets this firmly into his head.

"o.p.". (The explanation is a good instance of the "licence"
of § 1.) Associated with two entities x, y there is the o.p. (x, y):
the reader will understand "pair" (the class consisting of the two
entities—"class" is a primitive idea; see § 2); further e.g.
$(0, 1)$ is to be different from $(1, 0)$, and this is the intent of the
word "ordered". Similarly, of course, for e.g. "ordered triplet".

We shall often be saying "p implies q", where p and q are
certain propositions. When this occurs in the course of a proof
it asserts in effect that q is true if p is (and in such contexts p

is actually true, so we "have" q). The exact meaning (consistent with this) is "q is true or p is false" (or both, understood; this is the logical sense of "or").

"Function". Here, fortunately, we can build on a familiar basis. The reader has a firm grasp of what is ordinarily meant by (e.g.) a real function $f(x)$ of a real variable x: the "argument" x belongs to a certain class C of real numbers* (e.g. the class of all real numbers, or of all between 0 and 1); with each x of C there is associated exactly one "value" of the function, another real number, y say; and we express all this by saying that there is a function $f(x)$, defined for the range C of x, such that $f(x) = y$. To each x corresponds but one y, but the same y may of course correspond to more than one x. Two functions with the same range are different if and only if there is some x to which different y's correspond in the two cases.

To obtain the general idea of a function of one variable, we have merely to allow the "argument" x to range through any class of terms whatsoever (e.g. they may be numbers, classes, classes of classes, propositions), and the "values" $f(x)$ to come from any other (or of course the same) class of terms. The class through which the argument ranges we shall denote by $\mathcal{A}(f)$ (or $\mathcal{A}$ for short), that from which the values come $\mathcal{V}(f)$ (or $\mathcal{V}$). In the common case of two functions f_1, f_2 for which $\mathcal{A}_1 = \mathcal{A}(f_1)$ is contained in $\mathcal{A}_2 = \mathcal{A}(f_2)$ while $f_1(x) = f_2(x)$ whenever x belongs to $\mathcal{A}_1$ it is usual to say loosely that the function f_1 is the function f_2 "with its range confined to $\mathcal{A}_2$". It is better here to be very precise, and to count two such functions with different $\mathcal{A}$'s as different**.

If "$y = f(x)$" is a function of one variable x, consider the class K of all o.p. (x, y) for which the first term x ranges through $\mathcal{A}(f)$ and the second term y is the value of f associated with the 1st term. K is uniquely determined by f. Suppose, on the other hand, that K is any class of o.p. (x, y) with the restrictive prop-

---

* We are here taking for granted, of course, the idea of a real number.
** The $\mathcal{V}$'s raise no similar problem, since two functions with genuinely different $\mathcal{V}$'s are different on any view.

erty that no two o.p. of K have the same first term. This clearly determines an f with "$y = f(x)$". The conception of "function" therefore reduces to the conception of a K with the restrictive property, and this gives a final precision to the idea "function".*

What corresponds to a class of o.p. with the restrictive property dropped, i.e. a completely general class of o.p.? The answer is "a relation" (two-termed, "x has the relation R to y"). We take this up in Chapter II.

2. *Notion of class.* We shall regard this as a primitive idea. The letters A, B, C will be used to denote classes. A typical member (term) of A will be denoted by α, one of B by β, and so on. The relation (namely "is a") of a term α to the class A to which it belongs is denoted by $\alpha \varepsilon A$. The class whose sole member is α is denoted by (α).

A pair of classes A, B is said to be exclusive if no term x is common to both. Similarly for any set of exclusive classes; no term x is to be common to a (any) pair of the classes.

Addition of classes. Suppose we have a set of classes, a typical class of the set being A,** and suppose there is at least one class in the set (the set is not to be "null"). Then the "sum class" ΣA of the set is defined to be the class consisting of every term which belongs to some A of the set. (Terms belonging to more than one class of the set are to be "counted only once" in the sum class.) The sum class of A and B is denoted by A + B, that of A, B, C by A + B + C. [Note that in ΣA the "number" of A's need not be "finite"; that the sum class is independent of the idea of order (in particular A + B = B + A); that it is not necessary for an "infinite" set of classes to be capable of arrangement in a "series" for the sum class to exist; and that if there *is* an "infinite series" of A's, ΣA is a *real*

---

* A function of, say, two variables, $f(x, y)$, can be reduced to $f(z)$, in one variable z, where z ranges through the relevant class of o.p. (x, y).

** In future we abbreviate this to "set of classes A", with the understanding that it is the *classes* that have the names A, ... And with this understanding we could say "class of classes A" without ambiguity.

infinite sum, and not anything of the nature of a "limit". These negative statements are meant to correct natural prejudices; actually we do not as yet know the meaning of any of the words in inverted commas.]

Subtraction of classes. If B is contained in A, in symbols B ⊂ A, we mean by A − B the class of terms belonging to A but not to B.

Product of classes. The product II A of a set, containing at least one class, of classes A is the class consisting of all terms which belong to every A of the set. The product of A and B is written AB or A.B, and so on.

Identities. A sample pair are

(i) $X \Sigma A = \Sigma X A$;

(ii) if $P \subset A$ for each P of a set of classes P, then
$$A - \Sigma P = \Pi(A - P).$$

Take the second. If *x* belongs to the left side L, then for any P *x* belongs to A and not to P; so $x \varepsilon (A - P)$, and since this is true for every P, *x* belongs to $\Pi(A - P)$, which is the right hand side R: $x \varepsilon L$ implies $x \varepsilon R$. If on the other hand *x* does not belong to L it is either absent from A or belongs to some P; in either case there is a P such that *x* is absent from A − P and a fortiori from $\Pi(A - P)$: $x \notin L$ implies $x \notin R$. The two results establish that L = R.

It is easy, again, to verify *in any particular case* (a general proposition for "any finite number of classes" is quite another matter and belongs to § 23) that sums and products of classes obey the formal laws of addition and multiplication (this is of course the reason for our notation). After the sample proof just given we may leave the proof of similar things to the reader; they are no more difficult and go on similar lines.

3. *Similarity of classes.* The classes A and B are said to be similar (in symbols A ∼ B) if there is a correspondence between them in which every α has exactly one partner β, and *vice versa*: such a correspondence is called "one-one". Similarity is a

transitive and symmetrical relation; that is, if $A \sim B$ and $B \sim C$ then $A \sim C$, and if $A \sim B$ then $B \sim A$.

When a property of a set of classes A, B, ... is *necessarily* true of any set of (respectively) similar classes A′, B′, ... we may call the property "projective" (by obvious analogy).

The cardinal number of a class. We define the cardinal of a class A to be the class of all classes similar to A. This involves that similar classes have the same cardinal*, and this last property is the sole essential for further developments. Any definition which secured it would do equally well. [We may say, speaking roughly, that any projective property of classes can be expressed as a property of cardinals.]

We use the letters a, b, c, ... for cardinals. When a and A occur simultaneously we understand that A has cardinal a, and so on.

4. The *null class* is defined to be the class which has no members, i.e. the class Λ such that $x \epsilon \Lambda$ is false for every x. A *unit class* is a class which contains some term x, and is such that if y is a member of it, then $y = x$.

If A and B are null classes they are similar. If A and B are unit classes they are similar.

The cardinal of the null class is called 0, that of a unit class 1.

5. Given a pair of classes A, B we can certainly construct a pair A′, B′ of *exclusive* classes such that $A′ \sim A$, $B′ \sim B$. For let x, y be distinct entities. Let A′ be the class of o.p. (x, α), B′ that of pairs (y, β), where α and β run through A and B. Then A′ and B′ have the desired properties.

Lemma. Let A, B; A′, B′ be pairs of exclusive classes, and let A $\sim$ A′, B $\sim$ B′. Then $A′ + B′ \sim A + B$.

The proof is immediate.

Addition of cardinals. Given cardinals a, b, let A, B be exclusive classes of cardinals a, b respectively. A + B has by

* Also that every class has a cardinal.

the lemma a cardinal depending only on a, b; we define this cardinal to be $a + b$.

Since $A + B = B + A$ we have $a + b = b + a$. Also $(a + b) + c = a + (b + c)$, $a + 0 = a$.

We define $1 + 1 = 2$, $2 + 1 = 3$, and so on up to 9.

6. *Multiplication of cardinals.* Given a, b we take A, B en-clusive classes of cardinals a, b respectively. It is then easily proved that the class of o.p. (α, β), α running through A, β through B, has a cardinal that is independent of the special choice of A, B (i.e. is the same for a pair of exclusive similars A$'$, B$'$ as for A, B) and so dependent only on a, b. We define this cardinal to be $a \times b$ or ab. [We shall find ourselves unable to prove that the cardinal of a sum of a classes each of cardinal b depends only on a and b; we cannot therefore adopt the "usual" definition of multiplication in terms of addition.]

$$ab = ba. \qquad a(bc) = (ab)c. \qquad a(b + c) = ab + ac.$$

$$a \times 0 = 0. \qquad a \times 1 = a. \qquad a + a = 2a.\text{*}$$

If $ab = 0$, then either $a = 0$ or $b = 0$.

If $\amalg(a, b, c)$ is the cardinal of the class of ordered triplets (α, β, γ), α, β, γ running through exclusive A, B, C, then $\amalg(a, b, c) = abc$.

These easily proved propositions contain cases of the "as-sociative and commutative laws." We shall ultimately extend everything, by "induction", to cases of a "finite" number of car-dinals, but this must await a theory of "finite" and "induction".

7. *Exponentiation.* [The definition here also is not the "usual" one.] Let A, B be classes, of cardinals a, b, where $a \neq 0$, $b \neq 0$. Let P be the class of (all possible distinct) functions $f(\beta)$ for which $\mathcal{A}(f)$ is the class B and $\mathcal{V}(f)$ the class A. It is easily proved that p, the cardinal of P, is independent of the choice of A and B and depends only on a and b. We define ex-

* This is a *proposition*, not a definition (if we change a definition the old one becomes a proposition under the new one).

ponentiation (for a, $b \neq 0$) by $a^b = p$. We define also $a^0 = 1$ for $a \neq 0$, and $0^b = 0$ for $b \neq 0$. [0^0, the remaining combination, we do not define.]

[The genesis of the definition in common sense is, of course, "a kinds of things in b holes, the order of the holes counting".]

It is easily seen that $1^a = 1$.

The usual index laws are valid, and we shall find them powerful weapons.

Prop. 1. $a^b \times a^c = a^{b+c}$ *whenever either side exists.*

Prop. 2. $(ab)^c = a^c \times b^c$ *whenever either side exists.*

Prop. 3. $(a^b)^c = a^{bc}$, *unless a and one of b, c are 0.*

We give the proof of Prop. 3, as being the most difficult; the proofs of Props. 1 and 2 may be left to the reader.

The possible special cases in which one of a, b, c is 0 are easily verified. Supposing then that no one of a, b, c is 0, let A, B, C be exclusive classes of cardinals a, b, c. Let Φ be the class of functions $\alpha = \varphi(\beta)$, for which $\mathcal{U}(\varphi) = B$, $\mathcal{V}(\varphi) \subset A$; and let Ψ be the class of functions $\alpha = \psi(\beta, \gamma)$ of the two variables β, γ (β running through B, γ through C) with $\mathcal{U}(\psi) \subset A$. Since the o.p. (β, γ) are a class of cardinal bc, the cardinal of Ψ is $a^{(bc)}$. On the other hand, for each fixed γ, $\psi(\beta, \gamma)$, *qua* function of β, may be any φ, call it φ_γ. Thus Ψ is similar to the class of ways of attaching some φ from Φ to each γ of C. Its cardinal is accordingly

$$\text{(cardinal of } \Phi)^c = (a^b)^c.$$

This proves Prop. 3.

Examples. $a^1 = a$, $a^2 = a \times a$.

8. *Comparison of cardinals and classes.* Given two cardinals a and b, let A, B be corresponding classes. *If* A $\sim$ B *then* $a = b$. [Note that this is a proposition, not a definition of "="; see p. 2.] *If (and only if)* (part of A) $\sim$ B, *but* A $\sim$ B *is false,* we say $a > b$, $b < a$ (definitions of $>$, $<$). The relations between A, B are "projective", so the definitions are legitimate. "$a \geqslant b$" is

defined to mean "$a > b$ or $a = b$", and similarly for $\leqslant$. We have at once

Prop. 4. If (part A) $\sim$ B, *then* $a \geqslant b$. $a > b$ *and* $a < b$ *are incompatible.* $a > b$ *and* $a = b$ *are incompatible.*

The two outstanding questions are (i) must one of $>$, $<$, $=$ hold between a pair a, b; (ii) are $>$ and $<$ incompatible? We shall find ourselves unable to prove (i), and must make a distinction. We say that a, b are *commensurable* if one of $>$, $<$, $=$ holds between them, otherwise we say a, b are *incommensurable*. Similarly for classes A, B (note that either property is "projective").

To question (ii) the answer is "yes". But this is quite a difficult matter; we proceed to take it up.

9. In the lemma that follows we suppose A $\sim$ A$'$ by a correlation R; that P, Q,... are contained in A, and that for a typical P, P$'$ is the class whose members are correlated with those of P by R.

Lemma. (i) *If* P $\subset$ Q *then* P$'$ $\subset$ Q$'$ *and conversely.*

(ii) $(\Sigma P)' = \Sigma P'$ (*the summation being "the same" on each side*).

The proofs are easy.

Prop. 5. If a class is similar to a part of itself it is similar to any part containing this part.

Suppose that

(1)   A$'$ $\sim$ A by the correlation R; A$'$ $\subset$ A$_1$ $\subset$ A;

we have to prove that

(2)   A$_1$ $\sim$ A.

Let D = A $-$ A$_1$. We suppose D not null, else there is nothing to prove. We begin by considering the effect of subtracting D from A, and the correlate class D$'$ from each of A$'$ and A$_1$ (the subtractions are evidently possible). Since $A - D' \subset A_1 = A - D$ it is clear that the classes remaining, A^*, $A^{*\prime}$, A_1^*, say, satisfy all the relations in (1) (the correlation $A^{*\prime} \sim A^*$ being by R). If now a correlation[†] $A_1^* \sim A^*$ should happen to hold, we can combine it with $D' \sim D$ to obtain (2). The proof of (2) is thus "reduced" from the case A, A', A_1 to that of the smaller starred classes.

Other "reductions" may be possible, and it is natural to try whether we can prove (2) by pushing the reduction as far as possible. We define, generally, a "reduction of A, A', A_1 in respect of R" to be any process of subtracting classes H, H', H' from A, A', A_1 which yields ("reduced") classes A^*, $A^{*\prime}$, A_1^* satisfying

$$(1^*) \qquad A^{*\prime} \sim A^* \text{ by } R; \quad A^{*\prime} \subset A_1^* \subset A^*.$$

We observe that for *any* H contained in A all the relations in (1^*) are satisfied automatically except $A_1^* \subset A^*$. "Reducing" classes, or as we shall call them, classes H, are therefore those for which this remaining condition is satisfied; i.e. the classes H are those satisfying

$$(3) \qquad A_1 - H' \subset A - H.$$

We have seen that there *are* such classes, D being one (for that matter so is the null class Λ, and this would be enough to establish the essential fact that the set of H is not null).

Next: a reduction followed by a reduction is a reduction. More precisely:

(4) *If K is a reducing class of $A - H$, $A' - H'$, $A_1 - H'$ in respect of R, then $H + K$ is a reducing class of A, A', A_1 in respect of R.*

For

$$(A_1 - H') - K' \subset (A_1 - H) - K,$$

and so

$$A_1 - (H + K)' \subset A_1 - (H + K),$$

so that $H + K$ is an H, as desired.

[†] *This* correlation will, of course, generally *not* be by R.

Next, *any sum* $S = \Sigma H$ of H's (*not necessarily mutually exclusive*) *is an* H. For, by the Lemma and because $A_1 - H' \subset A - H$, we have [†]

$$A_1 - S' = A_1 - \Sigma H' = \Pi(A_1 - H') \subset \Pi(A - H)$$
$$= A - \Sigma H = A - S.$$

Now consider H_0, the sum of *all* H's and so itself an H, and let $A^* = A - H_0$, $A^{*}{}' = A' - H_0'$, $A_1^* = A_1 - H_0'$. We must have

(5) $A^* = A_1^*.$

For otherwise we can reduce further in respect of R by $D^* = A^* - A_1^*$ (as we saw to begin with); hence $H_0 + D^*$ is an H, by (4), so that $H_0 + D^* \subset H_0$, which contradicts $D^* \subset (A^* =) A - H_0$ (D^* being non-null). From (5) and $H_0' \sim H_0$ we have $A_1^* + H_0' \sim A^* + H_0$, which is $A_1 \sim A$, the desired result (2).

This is the proof arising most naturally from the idea of "reduction". There is, however, a less intuitive but very elegant proof of (5); if we incorporate this the proof of Prop. 5, stripped of explanations, reduces to the following very short one.

We define classes H to be those satisfying ($H \subset A$ and)

(3) $A_1 - H' \subset A - H.$

There are such classes (Λ, or $D = A - A_1$) [‡]. The class $H_0 = \Sigma H$, the sum of all H, is an H; for

$$A_1 - \Sigma H' = \Pi(A_1 - H') \subset \Pi(A - H) = A - \Sigma H;$$

this is, by the Lemma,

(6) $A_1 - H_0' \subset A - H_0.$

Next, subtracting both sides of (6) from A (and reversing the sense of $\subset$), we have

(7) $H_0 \subset D + H_0' = K,$

say. Taking correlates and then subtracting (with reversal of $\subset$)

[†] Note a double use of (ii) of §2.

[‡] So that there *is* a sum class ΣH. (A sum class exists only for a non-null *set* of classes, themselves possibly null.)

both sides from A_1 (A_1 contains any dashed set and DH_0' is null), we have, by the Lemma,

$$A_1 - K' \subset A_1 - H_0' = A - K.$$

That is, K is an H. Hence $K \subset H_0$, and, from (7)

$$H_0 = K = D + H_0'.$$

Subtracting both sides from A (DH_0' is null) we have

$$A_1 - H_0' = A - H_0$$

[which is (5)]. Combining with $H_0' \sim H_0$ we get $A_1 \sim A$.

It is surprising that so soon, and with such simple raw material (before we have even heard of "finite integer"), we should meet so deep a proposition and a proof involving so highly developed a mathematical technique.   The reader should note the coup of considering the sum of "all" H.   He has possibly not met anything quite like it before, but we shall meet things like it more than once again.

Prop. 6.   (*Schröder-Bernstein Theorem.*)   *If* $A \sim B_1$, *where* B_1 *is contained in* B, *and* $B \sim A_1$, *where* A *is contained in* A, *then* $A \sim B$.

By the first correlation A_1 is correlated with B_2 contained in B_1.   Thus $B \sim B_2$.   By Prop. 5, $B \sim B_1 \sim A$.

Prop. 7.   *If* $a \geqslant b$ *and* $a \leqslant b$, *then* $a = b$.   *Also* $a > b$, $a < b$ *are incompatible.*

Since > and =, < and =, are incompatible, it is enough to prove the second part.   If $a > b$, $a < b$ we have $B \sim A_1 \subset A$, $A \sim B_1 \subset B$.   Therefore $A \sim B$, and $a = b$, contrary, by Prop. 4, to (say) $a > b$.

10.   *Inequalities.*

Prop. 8.

   (i) $(a > b \text{ and } b \geqslant c)$ *implies* $a > c$.
   (ii) $(a \geqslant b \text{ and } b \geqslant c)$ *implies* $a \geqslant c$.

(iii) $(a \geqslant a_1$ and $b \geqslant b_1)$ implies $a + b \geqslant a_1 + b_1$ and implies
$$ab \geqslant a_1 b_1.$$

(iv) $a > c$ implies $a + b > c$.

(v) $a \geqslant a_1$ implies $a^b \geqslant a_1^b$.

(vi) $(b \geqslant b_1$ and $a \neq 0)$ implies $a^b \geqslant a^{b_1}$.

(vii) $a \geqslant 0$.

Inequalities are easy, false, or "unprovable" ["$(a > a_1, b > b_1)$ implies $a + b > a_1 + b_1$" is unprovable]. As samples take (i), (ii) and (iii).

(i) Choose classes A, B, C of cardinals a, b, c. Then *whatever* classes are chosen we have C $\sim$ (part B), B $\sim$ (part A), whence C $\sim$ (part A) and $a \geqslant c$; in particular this argument proves (ii). If $a = c$, then $b \geqslant c$ implies $b \geqslant a$, which is incompatible with $b < a$ by Props. 4 and 7.

(iii) (part A) $\sim$ A$_1$, (part B) $\sim$ B$_1$ together imply "some part of (A + B) is similar to A$_1$ + B$_1$". They also imply "some part of the class of o.p. (α, β) is similar to the class of (α_1, β_1)".

Prop. F. 1.† $1 > 0$.

(This is needed as the basis of an induction. The proof is easy.)

11. *Prop.* 9. *If* A *is similar to* B, *then the classes obtained by adding a* (new) *term to each of* A *and* B *are similar. If the subtraction of a term from each of* A *and* B *is possible, the remaining classes are similar.*

All this remains true if "similar" *is everywhere replaced by* "not similar".

(1) A $\sim$ B implies A + (x) $\sim$ B + (y).

(2) Let A $\sim$ B, A = A′ + (x), B = B′ + (y). If x and y correspond by $\sim$ we have A′ $\sim$ B′. If not let x correspond to y_1, y to x_1, and let A = A″ + (x) + (x$_1$), B = B″ + (y) + (y$_1$). The correspondence between A and B determines one between A″ and B″. Hence, by (1), A′ $\sim$ B′.

† Propositions F 1, 2 ... are about the "finite cardinals".

(3) Let A be not similar to B. If $A + (x) \sim B + (y)$ then $A \sim B$ by (2), a contradiction.

(4) Let A be not similar to B. If $A - (x) \sim B - (y)$ then $A \sim B$ by (1), a contradiction.

Prop. 10. *If A and B are commensurable or incommensurable classes, so are* $A + (x)$ *and* B, *and conversely.*

We may suppose that x does not belong to A. Then the *whole* prop. for incomm. follows from the whole prop. for comm., which we consider. The direct result is trivial unless $A \sim B_1$, where B_1 is a proper part of B. In this case let $y \varepsilon B - B_1$: clearly $A + (x) \sim B_1 + (y)$, which is contained in B.

The converse result is trivial unless $B \sim A_1$, A_1 is a proper part of $\{A + (x)\}$, and $x \varepsilon A_1$. Let $y \varepsilon A + (x) - A_1$. Clearly $A_1 + (y) - (x) \sim A_1$; and so $B \sim A_1 \sim A_1 + (y) - (x)$, which is contained in A.

12. We now translate these results into the language of cardinals. From *Prop.* 9 we have

Prop. 11. $a + 1 = b + 1$ *implies* $a = b$.
     $a + 1 \neq b + 1$ *implies* $a \neq b$, *and conversely.*

From *Prop.* 10 we have

Prop. 12. $a \mathrm{R} b$ *implies* $a + 1 \mathrm{R} b$, $a + 1 \mathrm{R} b + 1$.

     $a + 1 \mathrm{R} b$ *implies* $a \mathrm{R} b$.

     $a + 1 \mathrm{R} b + 1$ *implies* $a \mathrm{R} b$,

where R *denotes either of the relations comm. or incomm.*

13. *Prop.* 13. $a > b$ *implies* $a + 1 > b + 1$ *and conversely.*
     $a + 1 > b$ *implies* $a \geqslant b$.

(i) $a > b$ implies $a + 1 \geqslant b + 1$ (Prop. 8). But $a + 1 = b + 1$ implies $a = b$ (Prop. 11), and so *not* $(a > b)$ (Prop. 4). Hence $a + 1 > b + 1$. Again, if $a + 1 > b + 1$, then a comm. b (Prop.

12). But $a \leqslant b$ implies $a + 1 \leqslant b + 1$ (Prop. 8); false by Props. 7 and 4. Therefore $a > b$.

(ii) Let A and B have cardinals a and b, and let x not belong to A. $A + (x)$ has cardinal $a + 1$. Therefore B is similar to a proper part of $A + (x)$. Hence either $B \sim A_1$, a proper part of A, or $B \sim A$, or B is similar to a proper part $A_2 + (x)$ of $A + (x)$. In the first two cases $b \leqslant a$. In the third let $y \varepsilon A - A_2$, $A_3 = A - A_2 - (y)$. Then $B \sim A - (y) + (x) - A_3$, which is contained in $A - (y) + (x) \sim A$.

14. *The finite cardinals*. A class of cardinals is called *hereditary* if it contains $a + 1$ whenever it contains a. Hereditary classes exist, e.g. the class of all cardinals is hereditary. *A cardinal is called finite if (and only if) it belongs to* **every** *hereditary class that contains* 0. *All other cardinals are called infinite.*[*]

The reader will agree on reflection that this definition singles out those cardinals, and no others, that common sense regards as finite; will agree, therefore, that their properties must be all deducible from it. There is, however, a vague unexplained "and so on" in the common sense approach; our definition, on the other hand, is obviously unexceptionable.

Classes whose cardinals are finite or infinite are called finite or infinite.

Finite cardinals will be denoted by m, n.

Lemma. Finite cardinals exist, e.g. 0, 1.

0, and so also $0 + 1$, i.e. 1, belong to every hereditary class that contains 0.

Lemma. $n + 1$ is a finite cardinal (if n is).

The proof is immediate.

---

[*] Finite cardinals are also called inductive, or natural, cardinals, numbers, or integers.

Note the "all" coup in the definition.

Prop. F. 2. Suppose that $P(n)$ *is a propositional function such that* (*i*) $P(0)$ *is true,* (*ii*) *for each finite cardinal* n, $P(n)$ *implies* $P(n + 1)$. *Then* $P(n)$ *is true for every finite cardinal* n. ("Mathematical induction".)

Consider the class C of finite cardinals for which $P(n)$ is true. It is hereditary, by the hypothesis as to P *and the lemma*, and it contains 0. By the definition of a finite cardinal n belongs to it.

15. *Prop. F. 3. For every finite* n, $n + 1 > n$.

Call the proposition "$n + 1 > n$" $P(n)$. Then $P(0)$ is true, being Prop. F. 1; and "$P(n)$ implies $P(n + 1)$" is true, being part of Prop. 13. By Prop. F. 2 (or, as we shall often say in future, "by induction") $P(n)$ is true for every finite n.

16. We digress momentarily, in §16 only (the reader may ignore it if he wishes), to consider Peano's "indefinable and axiom" theory of "(finite) numbers". The indefinables are "0", "number", and "successor of". The axioms are as follows. (1) 0 is a number. (2) If n is a number, the successor of n is a number. (3) If two numbers have the same successor, the two numbers are identical. (4) 0 is not the successor of any number. (5) If C is a class to which belongs 0 and also the successor of every number belonging to C, then every number belongs to C. (See B. Russell, Introduction to Mathematical Philosophy, p. 5.)

It is possible to ask whether the axioms are consistent. A way of proving them consistent is to produce a set of 3 actual entities to represent the 3 indefinables which "satisfy" the axioms. This is done by *Prop. F. 4. If "number" is taken to mean finite cardinal, Peano's "0" to be our absolute 0, and "successor of* n" *to be* $n + 1$, *Peano's axioms are satisfied.*

The results are immediate except for (3). For this we have to show that $m + 1 = m' + 1$ implies $m = m'$, and this is given by Prop. 11.

17. *Prop. F. 5.* $m + n$, mn, m^n *are finite.*

(i) For fixed m the result is true for $n = 0$. Next $m + (n + 1)$ $= (m + n) + 1$ is finite if $m + n$ is. Therefore $m + n$ is always finite, by induction (applied to n).

(ii) $m(n + 1) = mn + m$, finite if mn is, by (i). Use induction.

(iii) $m^{n+1} = m^n \times m$, finite if m^n is, by (ii). Induction.

18. *Prop. 14. If $a \leqslant n$, then a is finite.*

This is true for $n = 0$; assume it true for n, and consider it for $n + 1$. Given $a \leqslant n + 1$ we have $a = n + 1$ or $a < n + 1$. In the first case a is finite; in the second $a \leqslant n$, by Prop. 13. The result is therefore true for $n + 1$. Induction.

Cor. A sub-class of a finite class is finite.

Lemma. a comm. n.

Clearly a comm. 0. Also a comm. $(n + 1)$ if a comm. n, by Prop. 12. Use induction.
From this follows

Prop. F. 6. Any two finite cardinals are commensurable.

Also

Prop. 15. If a is infinite (and n finite), then $a > n$.

For $a > n$ or $a \leqslant n$. In the second case we apply Prop. 14 to give a contradiction.

Cor. An infinite class contains (at least) n terms, where n is any finite cardinal. Conversely if $a \geqslant n$ for all n, then a is infinite.

If the converse is false we may take $n = a + 1$; then $a \geqslant a + 1$. This is false *if a is finite* (Props. 7 and F. 3).

19. *Prop. F. 7. There are exactly n cardinals (necessarily finite) less than n.*

This is true for $n = 0$ [Prop. 8 (vii)]; assume it for n, and consider it for $n + 1$. By Prop. 13 the numbers less than $n + 1$ comprise (i) the number n, and (ii) the numbers less than n. Class (i) has 1 member and class (ii) (by hypothesis) n members. Since by Prop. 4 the classes are exclusive, the cardinal of their sum class is $1 + n$, or $n + 1$. Prop. F. 7 is therefore true by induction.

Cor. There are exactly n cardinals greater than 0 and less than or equal to n. A class of n terms can be "labelled off" with the cardinals m satisfying $1 \leqslant m \leqslant n$.

For the two classes of n terms can be put in one-one correspondence.

20. *Prop. F. 8.* *If from a class of n terms we subtract m terms, where $m \leqslant n$, the cardinal of the remaining class depends only on m and n.*

If $n \geqslant m$ there exists a unique cardinal p, depending only on n and m, such that $n = m + p$.

In the first part let N be the number remaining. Clearly $N \leqslant n$ and is finite; also $N + m = n$. To dispose of both parts we have therefore only to prove that if $N + m = N' + m$ then $N = N'$.

This is true for $m = 0$; assume it for m. Now it follows from $N + (m + 1) = N' + (m + 1)$ that $(N + 1) + m = (N' + 1) + m$. [§5]. Hence $N + 1 = N' + 1$ and so $N = N'$. (Prop. 11). The result is true for $m + 1$. Induction.

Cor. If we subtract m terms from a class of $n + m$ terms, the remaining class has n terms.

These results enable us to define subtraction of a smaller from a larger finite cardinal.

21. *Prop. F. 9.* *Any non-null class of finite numbers has a least member, i.e. an n such that $n \leqslant m$ for all m of the class. Any **finite** non-null class of finite numbers has a greatest member.*

Let n_1 be a member of the class C. Let C_1 be the sub-class of distinct members m of C for which $m \leqslant n_1$. Clearly $n_1 \varepsilon C_1$. Since

$\leqslant$ is transitive and any two finite cardinals are commensurable, it is enough to prove the first part for C_1; therefore, since C_1 is finite (F. 7), for a finite non-null class. This follows by induction. Let C_1 have $N + 1$ members, and n_1 be one of them. $C_1 - (n_1)$ has N members, therefore a least member, n_2 say. The smaller of n_1, n_2 is a least member of C_1. Finally, the result is true when $N = 2$.

The second part is proved similarly.

Prop. F. 9 can be used as an alternative to an argument by induction; we argue: if $P(n)$ is not always true, let $n + 1$ be the first integer for which it is false. Then $P(n)$ is true, and if, as we are supposing, we know or can prove "$P(n)$ implies $P(n + 1)$" we get a contradiction.

Ordered finite sets.

If k is a finite non-zero integer an "ordered k-set" is a set of k terms x with the k suffixes m satisfying $1 \leqslant m \leqslant k$ "attached". We denote it for short by $(x_1, x_2, \ldots, x_k)$.

The ordered k-sets formed from the x of a class X are in one-one correspondence with the class of functions f for which $\mathcal{A}(f)$ is the class of m satisfying $1 \leqslant m \leqslant k$, and $\mathcal{U}(f) \subset X$.

An ordered finite set S is a set which is an ordered k-set for some finite non-zero k. Two S's are counted as different if they have different k's, or if they have the same k, but there is an m such that $x_m \neq x_m'$.

Any class of k terms can be "arranged" as an ordered k-set.

The "recurrence relation".

Prop. 16. *Suppose we are given a non-null class* X *of terms* x *and a function* $f(x)$ *with* $\mathcal{A}(f) = X$, $\mathcal{U}(f) \subset X$. *Then, given an* x_0 *of* X *there exists a set of* x_n, *one corresponding to each finite integer* n, *and such that*

$$(1) \qquad\qquad x_{n+1} = f(x_n) \qquad (n \geqslant 0).^{\dagger}$$

---

†This bracket notation indicates the range over which the preceding proposition is asserted. We shall use it frequently in the sequel, together with a similar notation to define a class; e.g. (y_m) $(1 \leqslant m \leqslant n)$ means the class of y_m for which m satisfies $1 \leqslant m \leqslant n$.

Also the set and its correspondence with the n is uniquely de-
termined when x_0 is given. [*That is, if $x_0' = x_0$, and $x_{n+1}' = f(x_n')$*
($n \geqslant 0$), then $x_n' = x_n$ ($n \geqslant 0$).]

Let $P_1(n)$ be the propositional function, with $\mathcal{C}(P_1)$ the class of
finite $n > 0$, "there exists *at least* 1 ordered n-set S_n of x's,
$(x_1, x_2, \ldots, x_n)$, satisfying

$$(C_n) \qquad x_1 = f(x_0), \qquad x_{m+1} = f(x_m)(1 \leqslant m \leqslant n)";$$

and let $P_2(n)$ be what $P_1(n)$ becomes when "*at least* 1" is replaced by "*not more than* 1". In the first place $P_2(n)$ is always
true. For if ν is the first instance of failure, two distinct sets
S_ν, S_ν' exist, but the sets $S_{\nu-1}$, $S_{\nu-1}'$ obtained by omitting the
last members of S_ν, S_ν' are identical, impossible since the omit-
ted members would be identical, as f's of identical things, and
S_ν, S_ν' identical after all.

Next, $P_1(n)$ implies $P_1(n + 1)$, since we obtain an appropriate
S_{n+1} by adding $f(x_n)$ at the end of the set S_n. Since $P_1(1)$ is true,
P_1 is always true, and so P_1, P_2 are both always true.

This being so, let us call the last term of S_n, uniquely determined since $P_2(n)$ is true, ξ_n. Induction shows that S_n is identical with $(\xi_1, \xi_2, \ldots, \xi_n)$. Consider now (ξ_n), the set of ξ_n for
all n. Since S_{n+1} satisfies (C_{n+1}) for all $n > 0$ we have, for all
$n > 0$,

$$\xi_1 = f(\xi_0), \quad \xi_{n+1} = f(\xi_n).$$

Thus the set (ξ_n) satisfies (1). If (ξ_n') is another such set,
then $(\xi_1', \xi_2', \ldots, \xi_n')$ satisfies (C_n), and $\xi_n' = \xi_n$ by $P_2(n)$. This
being true for all n the set (ξ_n) is unique.

Theorems on a finite number of classes and cardinals.

22. *Definition of "Multiplicative Class".* The M.C. *of a class
of classes* A *is the class* M *of classes* P, *each of which contains
exactly one member representative of each* A. (There may be no
classes P; in this case M is the null class.)

The A's may be thought of as constituencies, and a typical P
as a parliament, subject, however, to the provision that the same

person may be "Member of Parliament" (M.P.) for several constituencies. Note that P's are counted as distinct if the *representations* differ in any way; thus two distinct "parliaments"
may (if the A's are not exclusive) contain identical sets of
"persons".*

There is a useful equivalent to the M.C. A function $f(A)$ for
which $\hat{a}(f)$ is the class of A's we call a "selector-function for
the class of A's" if its values satisfy "$f(A)\varepsilon A$" for each A [the
value of $f(A)$ for each argument A is to be a member α of that A].
The class M′ of possible selector-functions (the distinctness of
two functions being interpreted as explained in §1) is in an obvious one-one correspondence with M (the M.C.): either is null if
the other is, and to a P of M there corresponds in M′ the function defined by $\alpha = f(A)$, where α is the representative of A in
P, and conversely.

Prop. 17. *The M.C. of a finite non-zero number of existent
exclusive classes is not null.*

Let n be the number of classes. The theorem is true for n
= 2.† Assume it for n classes, and consider $n + 1$. Let A be
one of them; n remain. Let P be a member of the M.C. of this
remainder. There exists an α belonging to A. Then, *by the case*
$n = 2$, P and α together constitute a term of the M.C. of the
$n + 1$ classes.

*Cor. Given a finite class $(a, b, \ldots)$ of cardinals, there exists
a similar class $(A, B, \ldots)$ of classes, A having cardinal a, B
having cardinal b, etc.*

Consider the (non-null) class A_1 whose members are all the
classes A that have cardinal a‡, the class B_1 corresponding

* If the classes A *are* exclusive the situation is simpler, and we
could define M as the class of classes P which have the property that
for each A the product AP has exactly one member. But we wish (and
even in the special case) to emphasize the aspect of "representation".

† The case $n = 2$ is a primitive proposition, and we have, of course,
used it often without explicit mention.

‡ Actually A_1 is the same entity as a.

similarly to b, and so on.   The M.C. of the class $(A_1, B_1, \ldots)$ has a member, which is the desired class $(A, B, \ldots)$.

Prop. 17 with the word "finite" removed is called the "Multiplicative Axiom".   We return to this later.

Suppose $(a, b, \ldots)$ is a *finite*** non-null class of cardinals. Let $(A, B, \ldots)$ be a corresponding class of classes (Prop. 17, Cor.), which we may suppose exclusive[†].   Let $A', B', \ldots$ be another set (respectively similar to $A, B, \ldots$).   There is a class, call it $\mathcal{R}_A$, of correlations R_A between A and A', and similarly $\mathcal{R}_B, \ldots$.   Then M, the M.C. of $\mathcal{R}_A, \mathcal{R}_B, \ldots$ (not null, by Prop. 17) contains a parliament P $(R_A, R_B, \ldots)$, of *simultaneous* correlations, R_A, "M.P. for $\mathcal{R}_A$", correlating A, A', R_B correlating $B, B', \ldots$.[‡]   By one obvious use of P we see that $\Sigma A' \sim \Sigma A$, and by another that the M.C. of $A', B', \ldots$ and that of $A, B, \ldots$ are similar.   The corresponding cardinals (of ΣA and the M.C. of $A, B, \ldots$) consequently depend only on the original set of cardinals $a, b, \ldots$ (not on the representing classes), and may be defined as $\Sigma(a, b, \ldots)$ $\Pi(a, b, \ldots)$ respectively.   These are easily seen to have the respective properties

$$\Sigma(a, b, c, \ldots) = a + \Sigma(b, c, \ldots),$$

$$\Pi(a, b, c, \ldots) = a \times \Pi(b, c, \ldots).$$

23. *Prop.* 18. *In Prop. 9 we may replace "a term" by "any finite number of terms", with a corresponding result in Prop. 10. In Props. 11 and 12 we may replace 1's by n's (sometimes by different n's). The associative and commutative laws may be generalised, and the connexion between addition and multiplica-*

**[Note on Peano's axioms]. This use of "finite" cannot possibly be an "indefinable" one.

[†]Compare §5. Here we must take distinct entities $x, y, \ldots$, one corresponding to each of $A, B, \ldots$.   An induction is not needed; they can be $1, 2, \ldots, n$, where n is the number of classes.

[‡]We have now used Prop. 17 twice, and each use would fail if the original set of cardinals was infinite. It is worth going into the arguments very carefully, because with infinite sets the literature is full of fallacies, resulting from an unnoticed assumption of "Mult. Ax.": this generally occurs just where the writer is off his guard; I hope the reader may be inoculated for life.

*tion, and multiplication and exponentiation, etc., all to a finite
number of classes or cardinals (themselves possibly infinite).*

As a specimen let us analyse the ideas implicit in (i), the
"dots" symbolism in "$a + b + \ldots$", and (ii) the commutative
law. Let there be a class C of n numbers $a, b, \ldots$, and let them
be assigned suffixes and written as c_m $(1 \leqslant m \leqslant n)$ (Prop. F. 7,
Cor.), in any manner M. Then there exists an ordered n-set S of
numbers s_m $(1 \leqslant m \leqslant n)$ satisfying $s_1 = c_1$, $s_{m+1} = s_m + c_{m+1}$
$(1 \leqslant m \leqslant n)$. Further s_n is the number $\Sigma(a, b, \ldots)$, and it depends only on C, and not on M or S. Moreover, if we are *given* M
then the set S, including "order", is unique. If we call this total
statement P(n), an induction, of which we may by now omit the
details, proves P(n) for all n. The total statement justifies the
use of a symbolism "$c_1 + c_2 + \ldots$", and also the assertion that
it "obeys the commutative law".

From now on we will allow ourselves to argue "naturally",
and without further analysis, wherever we deal with finite
numbers.

In a complete account we should at this point define negative
numbers, rational numbers, real numbers, and develop the usual
account of Analysis.

24. *Prop. 19. The class* S *of sub-classes* of* A *has a greater
cardinal than* A. *(Cantor.) Hence there is no cardinal which is
not exceeded by another.*

Each member of A constitutes a sub-class; hence $s \geqslant a$. We
have then to show $s \neq a$.

Suppose $s = a$, there is then a one-one correlation between S
and A. Let x be a typical member of A, $\sigma(x)$ its correlate in S.
Consider the class B of all x's (and no others) such that x is not
a member of $\sigma(x)$. B is a sub-class of A, i.e. a member of S; let
y be its correlate. If $y \varepsilon B$, then, by the definition of B, y is not a
member of $\sigma(y)$; i.e. [since $\sigma(y) = B$] y is not a member of B. If
y is not a member of B, then, by the definition of B, y is a member of $\sigma(y)$, or $y \varepsilon B$. In either case there is a contradiction.

---

* The whole class and the null class are counted as sub-classes.

Prop. 20. *The class* S *of sub-classes of* A *(cardinal a) has cardinal* 2^a.

Cor. $2^a > a$.

We may suppose $a > 0$, the result being true for $a = 0$. S is similar to the class of functions $f(\alpha)$ for which $\hat{u}(f)$ is A, and $\hat{v}(f)$ consists of the numbers 0 and 1. (A sub-class A_1 of A corresponds to an $f(\alpha)$ whose value is 1 for α's of A_1 and 0 otherwise. 1 and 0 are marks in the examination for entrance to A_1.)

Ξ_0 *and reflexiveness.*

25. *The cardinal of the class of finite cardinals, other than* 0, *is called* Ξ_0.

There exist n finite cardinals $\neq 0$, namely those $\leqslant n + 1$. Hence $\Xi_0 \geqslant n$ for all n. Hence by Prop. 15 and Cor.,

Prop. 21. $\Xi_0 > n$ *for every finite n, and* Ξ_0 *is infinite.*

A progression (without ordinal implication) is a class for which there is a *given* one-one correspondence with the class of n's other than 0. We indicate the correspondence by attaching the suffix n to the term correlated with n, and we speak of "the progression $x_1, x_2, \ldots$".

By definition a class of cardinal Ξ_0 ("an" Ξ_0) possesses *some* one-one correspondence with the n, and can (in many ways, unfortunately) be "arranged", or "denumerated", as a progression. We reserve the symbol "D" for classes which are finite or have cardinal Ξ_0. Such classes are called *denumerable*.

26. *Prop.* 22. *A sub-class of an* Ξ_0 *is finite or an* Ξ_0.

Let the Ξ_0 be denumerated as $x_1, x_2, \ldots$ and let S denote the sub-class. Either (i) there exists an n_0 such that x_n does not belong to S for $n > n_0$, or (ii) given any n_0, there exists an $n > n_0$, such that $x_n \varepsilon S$. In case (i) S is a sub-class of $(x_1, \ldots, x_{n_0})$, therefore finite by Prop. F. 7 Cor. In case (ii) let $\varphi(n)$ be the *least* n' for which $n' > n$ and $x_{n'} \varepsilon S$. By Prop. 16 there exists a progression n_1, n_2, ... with $n_1 = 1$, $n_{r+1} = \varphi(n_r)$. Since $\varphi(n)$ > n we have $n_{r+1} > n_r$, and by induction $n_r > n_s$ for $r > s$. Hence the n_r are all different, and x_{n_1}, x_{n_2}, ... are (distinct) members of S; they form a progression; S contains an Ξ_0, $s \geqslant \Xi_0$. But $s \leqslant \Xi_0$ and so $s = \Xi_0$.

Cor. 1. *An infinite sub-class of an* Ξ_0 *is an* Ξ_0.

Cor. 2. *If we subtract a finite class from an* Ξ_0 *an* Ξ_0 *remains.*

Cor. 3. *If* $a \leqslant \Xi_0$ *a is finite or* $a = \Xi_0$. *If* $a < \Xi_0$ *then a is finite.*

27. *Definition.* A reflexive class is one which is similar to a *proper* part of itself. A reflexive cardinal is the cardinal of a reflexive class. [We need the usual independence theorem.]

Prop. 23. *A necessary and sufficient condition that a class should contain an* Ξ_0 *is that it should be reflexive.*

(i) If A contains an Ξ_0, D, let

$$A = D + A' = (x_1) + (x_2) + \ldots + A'.$$
$$A - \quad (x_1) \quad = (x_2) + (x_3) + \ldots + A'.$$

There is an obvious correlation between A and A $-$ (x_1): A is reflexive.

(ii) If A is reflexive A $\sim$ A$'$, a proper part of A. Let $\varphi(x)$ denote the correlate in A$'$ of x in A. There exists an x_0 belonging to A but not to A$'$.

Consider the progression x_1, x_2, ... defined (Prop. 16) by $x_{n+1} = \varphi(x_n)(n \geqslant 0)$. This gives an Ξ_0 contained in A provided no two x's of the progression are identical. Suppose this provision false, and let m be the least suffix (Prop. F. 9) for which x_m = another x of the sequence, say $x_m = x_n$, $n > m \geqslant 1$. This is $\varphi(x_{m-1}) = \varphi(x_{n-1})$; hence, by the fact that the correlation represented by φ is one-one, we must have $x_{m-1} = x_{n-1}$. If $m > 1$ this contradicts the hypothesis that m is the least suffix. If $m = 1$ x_{m-1} is x_0, which is not in A$'$, while x_{n-1} has a positive suffix and is in A$'$, and their identity is impossible.

28. *Prop. 24. The cardinal of a reflexive class is unaltered (i) when we subtract a finite number of terms from the class, (ii) when we add a finite number of terms, or an E_0.*

Take (ii) first. Let $A = D + A'$, D an E_0. It is enough to prove that adding n or E_0 terms to D leaves its cardinal E_0. Let D be $x_1, x_2, \ldots$, and the added class $y_1, y_2, \ldots$, terminating or not. The sum can be "arranged" as $x_1, y_1, x_2, y_2, \ldots$, and is denumerable.

The "n^{th} term in the arrangement counting from left to right" (the term for which the number of predecessors is $n - 1$) is the term to be correlated with n in the denumeration. This conveys the essential idea very briefly where, as sometimes happens, the full statement of which x or y is to be correlated with n would be very cumbrous.

Consider now (i). The theorem is clearly true for an E_0 $x_1, x_2, \ldots$, since an E_0 remains when we suppress a finite number of terms (Prop. 22, Cor. 2). In the general case $A = D + A'$, suppose m terms are suppressed in D and m' in A′. We may replace the missing terms in A′ by the first m' terms of D not already suppressed; the new D can be correlated with the old, and the new A′ with the old.

Cor. 1. The sum class of a finite number of E_0's is an E_0.

Cor. 2. A necessary and sufficient condition that $a \geqslant E_0$ is that $a + 1 = a$. If $a + 1 = a$, we have also $a + n = a$, and $a + E_0 = a$.

Prop. 25. If $A = D + A'$ and A′ contains an E_0, then A and A′ have the same cardinal.

For A′ is reflexive; apply Prop. 24 (ii).

29. *Prop. 26. Suppose $n > 0$. Then*

$$E_0 + E_0 + \ldots (n \text{ terms}) = E_0.$$

$$E_0 + n = E_0.$$

$$E_0^2 = E_0, \quad E_0^n = E_0.$$

$$n E_0 = E_0.$$

Each left hand side is greater than or equal to Ξ_0; it is therefore enough to prove it less than or equal to Ξ_0. $\Xi_0 \times \Xi_0$ is the cardinal of the class of o.p. (x, y), x ranging through the x_n, y through the y_n. These o.p. can be denumerated as*

$$(x_1, y_1), (x_1, y_2), (x_2, y_1), (x_1, y_3), (x_2, y_2), (x_3, y_1), \ldots.$$

Thus $\Xi_0 \times \Xi_0 = \Xi_0$. The left hand side is Ξ_0^2 (Examples, Prop. 3); hence $\Xi_0^2 = \Xi_0$. $\Xi_0^n = \Xi_0$ follows by induction.

The other left hand sides are less than or equal to Ξ_0^2.

Important special classes of cardinal Ξ_0.

30. It is simplest to go straight to a very general theorem. Suppose k is any finite non-zero integer, and let us denote by S, by S_k, or, still more fully, by $S_k(n_1, n_2, \ldots, n_k)$, any ordered k-set of finite integers. We have

Prop. 27. The class of all ordered finite sets of integers has cardinal Ξ_0.

We need prove only that the cardinal is less than or equal to Ξ_0, since the sub-class of S_1's is an Ξ_0.

With $S_k(n_1, n_2, \ldots, n_k)$ we associate the integer

$$N = 2^{n_1+1} \cdot 3^{n_2+1} \cdot \ldots \cdot p_k^{n_k+1},$$

in which p_m is the mth prime. By the theorem of unique factorization distinct S must have distinct N, and the class of all S is in one-one correspondence with a sub-class of the positive integers, whence the desired result.

Cor. 1. If a class of terms x is denumerable the class of ordered finite sets of x's is denumerable.

Cor. 2. The class of rational numbers is denumerable.

Cor. 3. The class of algebraic numbers is denumerable.

Cor. 1 is an immediate consequence of the main theorem.

* This process is called the "diagonal method."

In *Cor.* 2 any rational can be written, uniquely, in the form $(-1)^n p/q$, where p and q are relatively prime, and $n = 0$ or 1, and the rationals are in one-one correspondence with the class of ordered triplets (n, p, q), a sub-class of the class of all ordered triplets.

By *Cor.* 1 and *Cor.* 2 the class of all ordered finite sets R of rationals can be denumerated as $R_1, R_2, \ldots$. An algebraic (complex) number x is the root of an equation

(E) $$x^n + a_1 x^{n-1} + \ldots + a_n = 0,$$

where the a's are rationals. The distinct roots of (E) can be arranged as $x_1, x_2, \ldots$ according to some fixed rule (say in order of increasing real part, and of increasing imaginary part where real parts are equal). Let our x be x_m. With x and each (E) of which it is a root (and there will be many) we associate the set $(m, n, a_1, a_2, \ldots, a_n)$. This is some R, R_ν say. Let ν_0 be the least ν such that R_ν is associated with x in this way. Different x are seen at once to have different ν_0, and this shows that the class of x is denumerable. Also it certainly contains an Ξ_0.

31. *Prop.* 28.   *The class of all "rational spheres" in all Euclidean spaces of finite numbers of dimensions is denumerable.*

A point P of the Euclidean space of k dimensions is an ordered k-set $(x_1, x_2, \ldots, x_k)$ of real numbers. The distance PP' is $\left\{ \Sigma (x_m - x_m')^2 \right\}^{\frac{1}{2}}$, and a sphere of centre Q and radius r is the set of points P such that $PQ < r$. A rational sphere is one with rational radius r and with a point with rational coordinates $(x_1, x_2, \ldots, x_k)$ for its centre. This sphere is uniquely associated with the $(k + 1)$-set $(r, x_1, x_2, \ldots, x_k)$, and the class of all such sets (k varying) is denumerable.

We suppose this class of rational spheres denumerated once for all in a fixed manner as $S_1, S_2, \ldots$. Any rational sphere in any Euclidean space is an S of this progression with a definite suffix.

Prop. 29.   *A class of non-overlapping intervals on a straight line, or, more generally, a class of non-overlapping "spheres" or "rectangles" in a Euclidean space of any finite number of dimensions, is denumerable.*

Each "volume" V (sphere or rectangle) of the class certainly contains rational spheres of the space strictly in its interior. We can associate with V that contained sphere S_n which has least suffix in the progression. Non-overlapping V's correspond evidently to different S_n, and the class of V's must be denumerable.

We may observe that precisely the same argument applies when the V's are replaced by any non-overlapping "open sets". (We shall meet these in Chapter IV.)

32. *Lemma. If a class A of cardinal a contains b exclusive sub-classes, then $2^a \geqslant 2^b$.*

Paradoxical as it may seem, we cannot prove $a \geqslant b$ (without assuming a "selection axiom"; see §38 below). The Lemma is a second-best.

Let S be a typical one of the *b* sub-classes. Think of an S as a "bag" containing α's of A. We have to prove that the number of distinct sets of bags is less than or equal to the number of distinct sets of α's (the numbers being 2^b and 2^a respectively). If Σ, Σ' are two distinct sets of S, the sets of α's derived from Σ, Σ' by "opening" the bags are also distinct. There are therefore not more Σ's than there are sets of α's.

Prop. 30. *If q is infinite then a class of cardinal 2^q contains Ξ_0 exclusive non-null sub-classes. Also $2^{2^q} \geqslant 2^{\Xi_0} > \Xi_0$.*

Another paradox: we cannot disprove the possibility that an infinite q (initial of "queer") may be incommensurable with Ξ_0 (and incidentally non-denumerable and so non-reflexive [Prop. 23], $q + 1 > q$). Prop. 30 is a second-best.

Let Q be a class of cardinal q and A the class of all sub-classes σ of Q, so that A has cardinal $a = 2^q$. For $n \geqslant 1$ let S_n be the class of all those σ's that have exactly n members. Since q is infinite no S_n is null. If $n \neq m$ S_n and S_m are two exclusive classes of σ's (a σ of S_n has a different number of members from one of S_m). So S_1, S_2, ... are a set, $b = \overline{E}_0$ in number, of exclusive non-null classes of σ's, and each S is contained in A (the class of *all* σ's). This proves the first part; the second follows by the Lemma.

33. *The cardinal c.* This is defined to be the cardinal of the class of all real numbers.

Prop. 31. The class of x's such that $a < x < \beta$ ($\beta > \alpha$) has cardinal c.

For $y = z/(1 - z^2)$ is a one-one correlation between the class of all real y and the class of z for which $-1 < z < 1$, and $z = (2x - \alpha - \beta)/(\beta - \alpha)$ is one between the class of z and the class of x for which $\alpha < x < \beta$.

In particular c is the cardinal of the class of x for which $0 < x < 1$.

Cor. The result remains true if we add one or both of α and β to the class.

For the class of x contains an $\overline{E}_0$, for example,

$$(\alpha + n\beta)/(1 + n) \quad (n = 1, 2, \ldots),$$

and the Cor. follows by Prop. 25.

34. *Prop. 32.* $c = 2^{\overline{E}_0}$.

Let Γ be the class of binary decimals. Owing to the double representation ($\dot{0}$ and $\dot{1}$) this is similar to the class C of x such that $0 < x \leqslant 1$, *plus* the class T of terminating decimals. T has $\overline{E}_0$ terms, by Prop. 27. The cardinal of Γ is $2^{\overline{E}_0}$ (there are $\overline{E}_0$ places filled by 0's and 1's). When we remove the $\overline{E}_0$ T from Γ, we have left C, which we have seen contains an $\overline{E}_0$. Therefore (by Prop. 25) we do not thus alter the cardinal of Γ. Hence $2^{\overline{E}_0} = c$.

Cor. $c \geqslant \overline{E}_0$.

We want in practice, however, more than this.

35. *Prop. 33. A class of cardinal c remains of cardinal c after the suppression of any Ξ_0 of its terms.*

By Prop. 25 it is enough to show that whatever Ξ_0 is suppressed in a class C of cardinal c an Ξ_0 remains.

C is correlated with C_0, the class of x satisfying $0 \leqslant x < 1$, and it is enough to prove the last result for C_0.

Let the Ξ_0 be $x_1, x_2, \ldots,$ or D, and let the decimal representations of the x's be (9 not permitted):

$$x_1 = {\cdot}a_1{}^1 a_2{}^2 \ldots$$
$$\ldots\ldots$$
$$x_n = {\cdot}a_1{}^n a_2{}^n \ldots$$
$$\ldots\ldots$$

Consider $\qquad y_1 = {\cdot}b_1 b_2 \ldots,$ $\qquad\qquad$ where

$$b_n = 1, 2, 3, 4, 5, 6, 7, 8, \underline{7}\ 0$$

according as $\qquad a_n{}^n = 0, 1, 2, 3, 4, 5, 6, 7, 8, 9$ $\qquad$ (1)

Then $0 \leqslant y_1 < 1$, and 9 cannot occur in y_1. y_1 is different from x_n (in the nth place) for every n, and (since the representations as decimals are unique) is not one of D. Further, rule (1) being fixed, y_1 is uniquely determined by the progression $x_1, x_2, \ldots$. Now $y_1, x_1, x_2, \ldots$ is a progression, and determines y_2 different from y_1 and not in D. And so on. The process determines uniquely an $\Xi_0, y_1, y_2, \ldots,$ contained in $C_0 - D$.

Example. The class of irrationals, or of transcendants, between 0 and 1 has cardinal c.

36. *Prop. 34. If $n \geqslant 1$ and is finite*

$$c^{\Xi_0} = c^n = \Xi_0{}^{\Xi_0} = (n + 1)^{\Xi_0} = 2^{\Xi_0} = \Xi_0 c = nc = c.$$

For $\qquad\qquad c^{\Xi_0} = (2^{\Xi_0})^{\Xi_0} = 2^{\Xi_0 \times \Xi_0} = 2^{\Xi_0} = c,$

c^n lies between c^{Ξ_0} and c, $(n + 1)^{\Xi_0}$ and $\Xi_0{}^{\Xi_0}$ between c^{Ξ_0} and 2^{Ξ_0}, nc and $\Xi_0 c$ between $c.c$ and $1.c$.

Prop. 35.   *The class of points in space of n dimensions has cardinal c.*

Its cardinal is $c^n = c$.

Prop. 36.   *The class of functions of a real variable has cardinal $2^c > c$.*

Its cardinal is $c^c = (2^{\aleph_0})^c = 2^{\aleph_0 c} = 2^c$. ("*c* kinds of things in *c* holes")

Prop. 37.   *The class of continuous functions of a real variable has cardinal c.*

Arrange the rationals as a progression (x_n). Consider the class of functions F defined only at (x_n). Its cardinal is $c^{\aleph_0} = c$. If $f(x)$ is any continuous function of x and F is the function defined only at (x_n) and such that $F(x_n) = f(x_n)$, f is determined when F is given. (The value of an f at x is the limit of f through a subsequence of the (x_n) tending to x: if two f's agree at all x_n they must agree at all x.) Thus the f's are correlated with a sub-class of the class of F, and their class has cardinal c at most. It has cardinal c at least since the sub-class of constant functions has.

Cor. There exists a function $\varphi(x, \alpha)$, continuous in x for fixed α, which represents each continuous function of x for a suitable value, and one value only, of α.

37. Let A be a class of cardinal $a > 1$, α a typical member of A. The class of progressions of α's has cardinal $a^{\aleph_0}$. The value of this is c when a is finite (and greater than 1), when $a = \aleph_0$, and when $a = c$. Thus there are c distinct progressions formed with 0's and 1's, c distinct progressions formed with integers, c distinct progressions of real numbers. A progression being an "ordered $\aleph_0$-set" the middle result may be contrasted with Prop. 28.

The Multiplicative Axiom.

38. Suppose we try to prove that an infinite class A contains an Ξ_0. We naturally proceed somewhat as follows:

A has a member, select one, x_1;

A $-$ (x_1) has a member, select one, x_2;

and so on.

We have here an infinity of arbitrary selections, each depending on the one before. The assertion, in these circumstances, of the existence of a progression x_1, x_2, ... is a proposition, or axiom, not used elsewhere in mathematics. It has not been deduced from the fundamental axioms from which the rest of mathematics has been shown to follow, and the question arises whether it is true. Reflection makes the intuition of its truth doubtful, analysing it into prejudices derived from the finite case, and short of intuition there seems no evidence in its favour. In any case it is important to distinguish the propositions which do not require it.

It is possible in all relevant cases to avoid at any rate the dependence of each choice on others (*previous* ones in the case of an Ξ_0 of choices); everything we should like to prove or to be true follows from a single assumption, called Mult. Ax. This asserts that *the Multiplicative class of a non-null class of non-null classes is non-null.*

The following "Selection Axiom" is an equivalent to Mult. Ax. *If no one of the classes* A *is null there exists a selector-function* φ *such that for each* A $\varphi(A) = \alpha$, *where* α *belongs to* A. (Compare §22.)

The axiom is only an assumption when the number of A's is infinite (Prop. 16). When the number of terms in each A is finite, there is no simplification; an infinite class of pairs has all the characteristic difficulty.

39. *Consequences of Mult. Ax.*

(1) *The sum class of a exclusive classes* B *each of cardinal b has cardinal ab.*

We may suppose $a > 0$, $b > 0$, other cases being trivial. Fix a class B_1 of cardinal b. Each B has a set $\aleph_B$ of correlations with B_1; we select a set of "representative" correlations R_B, one for each B, R_B (M.P. for $\aleph_B$) correlating B with B_1. The cardinal of this class is, of course, a. Each β_1 of B_1 is thus joined to one unique term in each B, the various β_1-joins corresponding each to different R_B's and each R_B containing one β_1-join. The number of terms in the sum-class ΣB = total number of joins = number of pairs (β_1, R_B) = ba.

Cor.   *An Ξ_0 of Ξ_0's is an Ξ_0 of terms.*

For its cardinal is $\Xi_0 \cdot \Xi_0 = \Xi_0$.

This result dominates the whole theory of Lebesgue measure; without Mult. Ax. the theory would be intolerably cumbrous and restricted.

(2) *The sum of an infinite number of cardinals b can be defined.*

Given a class (whose members are cardinals b), there exists a class Γ of corresponding *classes* B. *This requires Mult. Ax.* The B's may be supposed mutually exclusive. Consider another class of classes B′, where B′ $\sim$ B. We can select by Mult. Ax., for each pair B, B′, one correlation out of the possible ones, thus obtaining a class of correlations, one for each B, B′. Combining these we have evidently $\Sigma B \sim \Sigma B'$, and the common cardinal may be taken as the meaning of Σb.

Cor. 1. $\Sigma b \geqslant$ *any particular b of the sum.*

Cor. 2.   *The sum of a progression of strictly increasing cardinals is greater than any cardinal of the progression.*

For $\Sigma b_n \geqslant b_{n+1} > b_n$.

(3) *Πb can be defined for an infinite set of b's.*

As above, there exists, by Mult. Ax., a corresponding class of classes B, which may be supposed exclusive. Given another class of classes B′, let C be the M.C. of the B, C′ that of the B′. As above, we form, by Mult. Ax., a class of correlations, one between each B, B′. This gives C $\sim$ C′, and the common cardinal

c is defined to be the value of Πb. (By a third application of Mult. Ax. the class C is not null, and $\Pi b > 0$, if none of the b's is zero.)

N.B.——The Mult. *class* of a class of B's can be defined without Mult. Ax., though we cannot show it is not null. We cannot so define a *product of cardinals*.

(4) *Given a class of b cardinals each equal to a, their sum is ab and their product ab.*

(This may be left to the reader: compare (1).)

(5) *If A contains b exclusive non-null classes, then $a \geqslant b$.*

(Compare §32. We take a representative term for each "bag".)

(6) *An infinite class A contains an Ξ_0 (and is reflexive).*

Let S be the class of non-null sub-classes σ of A. There is a selector-function $\varphi(\sigma)$ such that $x = \varphi(\sigma)$ and $x\varepsilon\sigma$. [The x's, of course, are not all different.] Let

$$x_0 = \varphi(A), \quad A_1 = A - (x_0), \quad x_1 = \varphi(A_1),$$
$$A_2 = A_1 - (x_1), \quad x_2 = \varphi(A_2),$$
$$\cdots$$

The process cannot exhaust A at any stage, since A has more than n terms whatever n is. Also x_n is different from $x_0, x_1, \ldots, x_{n-1}$, which are absent from A_n. Hence we obtain an Ξ_0 (x_n) contained in A.

Cor. A non-denumerable class has cardinal greater than Ξ_0, and its cardinal is unaltered by the removal of any Ξ_0 terms.

For after the removal, the remainder is not finite (or the original would be an Ξ_0); being, therefore, infinite it contains an Ξ_0, by the proposition, and by Prop. 25 the cardinal is unaltered. Also, since the class contains an Ξ_0 without being an Ξ_0 its cardinal is greater than Ξ_0.

With Mult. Ax. a non-denumerable set is "very large"; without it it need only be queer (a Q; see §32).

Further consequences of Mult. Ax. must be deferred for the present.

CHAPTER II.

Well-ordered Series

1. After the reduction of a "function" of a variable x $[f(x)]$ to a special class of o.p. the reader will make no difficulty about reducing a relation xRy to an unrestricted class of o.p. (as mentioned in §1). We are now to be specially concerned with relations of "order".

There is a common sense idea of "order* among the terms of a class, or 'field'", and though there are many varieties a mathematician instinctively pictures it as like order on a line from left to right. A point on the left "precedes" one on the right; the general idea is "x precedes y", xPy for short. Common sense requires a P to have, for terms x, y, ... of the field "ordered" by P, the properties: (1) if x, y are different, then either xPy or yPx, but xPx is false; (2) if xPy is true then yPx is false; (3) if xPy and yPz then xPz. (These forms are chosen for perspicuity, not logical refinements such as non-redundancy.) A little experiment and reflection will convince the reader, first that any proposition that is purely about order† can be deduced from (1), (2) and (3), secondly that any relation P satisfying them does satisfactorily "order" its field. (1), (2) and (3) are the "axioms of order", and an ordering relation P is to be any relation satisfying them. In the reduction to o.p. P is represented by a field F of terms and a class K of o.p., (x, y) satisfying the axioms (1) if x, y are different terms of F then either (x, y) or (y, x) belongs to K, but if x is a term of F (x, x) does not belong to K; (2) if x, y are terms of F and (x, y) belong to K, (y, x) does not; (3) if x, y, z are terms of F and (x, y), (y, z) belong to K then (x, z) belongs to K.

---

* Understood to exclude cyclic order.

† For example: if y and z are different, and between x and w, then y is between x and z or between z and w, and the alternatives are exclusive. "Between" has an obvious definition in terms of "precedes".

Along with the relation P——"precedes"——we take over the terms usually associated with the word "precedes": "succeeds", "predecessor" ["successor"], "immediate predecessor", of a term or of a class of terms, "between", "first", "last"; the definitions of all of them are obvious.

A field ordered by a P is called a "series".

Two series are said to be *ordinally similar* (or, for brevity, similar) if there exists a one-one correspondence between their terms which "preserves the order", i.e. a one-one correspondence in which if x', y' correspond to any x, y, then x' precedes y' if x precedes y. Ordinal similarity is clearly transitive.

2. *A well-ordered series is a series in which every non-null sub-series* has a first term.* (For brevity we write W for "well-ordered series".) Evidently a series ordinally similar to a W is a W. This definition implies that (1) *the series has a first term*; (2) *every class of terms which has successors in the series has an immediate successor.*

(1) is obvious. For (2) consider the series of successors of the given class. This is not null, by hypothesis, and therefore has a first term. This is the required immediate successor.

In particular every term has an immediate successor if it has any successors. But a term need not have an immediate predecessor.

We use the symbols A, B, ..., W_1, ... for W's.

3. *Prop. 1. (Transfinite Induction). Let* $\Pi(x)$ *be a propositional function whose* $\mathcal{U}(\Pi)$ *consists of the terms of a W, and with the properties*: (1) $\Pi(x_0)$ *is true for the first term* x_0 *of W,* (2) *the truth of* $\Pi(y)$ *for all y preceding x implies* $\Pi(x)$. *Then* $\Pi(x)$ *is true for all x of W.*

Consider the sub-series of terms for which Π is false. If not null, it has a first term x. By (1) x is not x_0. $\Pi(y)$ is true for every y preceding x. By (2) $\Pi(x)$ is true, and this is a contradiction.

* A sub-series of a given series is constituted by a sub-class of the terms, ordered by the original ordering relation. We sometimes use the term "part" to mean "sub-series".

We break off at this point to make some general observations about ordinary, or "mathematical" induction and transfinite induction (O.I. and T.I. for short). The digression is not essential to the rest of the Chapter; the reader may postpone it if he wishes till after §11 (or return to it then).

Prop. F. 2, the theorem of O.I., is deduced from the definition of finite cardinals; the deduction, however, is "slight", and we may say roughly that the finite cardinals are defined to be those on which O.I. works. Prop. F. 9 is a further deduction, but again a slight one, and, as we remarked in §21, Chapter I, F. 9 (with "first failure" and *reductio ad absurdum*) is an alternative weapon of argument to O.I. (F. 2). With T.I. there is a certain reversal of roles to begin with; a generalization of the (main) result of F. 9 is taken as a definition (of being a W), and the theorem of T.I., Prop. 1, is a deduction. The deduction is again slight, and we may roughly say that W's are those series on which T.I. works; here, again, T.I. on the one hand, and "first failure" with *reductio ad absurdum* on the other, are alternative weapons. W's and T.I. are a result of pushing "induction" as far as it will go.

The connection of W's with T.I. is actually "characteristic". We have seen that W's obey T.I. But conversely we have the following result:

Let S be a series with a first term x_0; we say that a propositional function $\Pi(x)$, with $\mathcal{U}(\Pi)$ the terms of S, is "hereditary in S" if it has the property that "$\Pi(x)$ for all x preceeding y" implies $\Pi(y)$. Suppose now S has the property that every $\Pi(x)$ hereditary in S, and for which $\Pi(x_0)$ is true, is necessarily true for all x of S. Then S is a W.

This depends on the Lemma, of which we may leave the proof as an exercise for the reader:

Let S_x be the sub-series of S consisting of the terms of S preceding x: if now every S_x is a W, then S is a W.

Granted the Lemma, we prove the theorem by taking $\Pi(x)$ to be the particular propositional function "S_x is a W".

The principles O.I. and T.I. are "propositions about a proposition*". The present result is accordingly a proposition about a proposition about a proposition.

4. *Prop.* 2. *Every sub-series of a W is a W.*

Let A be a W, B a sub-series of A. We have to show that every sub-series of B has a first term. This is obvious, since the sub-series is a sub-series of A.

Consider the series (it *is* one) of the finite cardinals, ordered by the relation <. It is a W (Prop. F. 9). Any ordinally similar series is called a *progression*. Incidentally we see that W's exist.

5. *Prop.* 3. *A descending W of terms in a W is finite (the class of the terms is finite).* [We must not write "series" for the first "W".]

Suppose not. Then for every n the descending W has at least n terms, the nth term (i.e. the term with exactly $(n - 1)$ predecessors in the descending W) is unique (induction), and the descending W begins with a progression D. D is a part of the W which has no first term (in the original order). Etc.

6. *Prop.* 4. *The ordinal correlation between two ordinally similar W's is unique.*

If not let there be two. Consider the class of terms that have different partners in the two correlations. There is a first, x_1 say, correlated with x_2 and x_2' in the two correlations, where, say, x_2' succeeds x_2. Let $\bar{x}_1$ be the correlate of x_2 in the second correlation. It precedes x_1 since x_2 precedes x_2'; also its correlate is x_2 in the second, and not in the first, correlation. Thus x_1 is not the first x with different correlates.

7. *Sections.* *A section of a W by an element x is the W of terms which precede x.* It is a W by Prop. 2.

* More strictly, a propositional function.

In an ordinal correlation sections correspond to sections.

Definition. Of two different sections A, B, *we say that* A > B *or* A < B *according as the term of the* W *determining* A *succeeds or precedes that determining* B. (One of the two must hold.)

Prop. 5. A W *cannot be ordinally similar to a section of itself.* (This is not true if for "section" we read "part".)

For suppose A ~ A_1, a section of A corresponding to the term a. Let x_1 be the first term* of A_1 not correlated with "itself", and let its correlate in A be x. Then x succeeds x_1, for otherwise it must be correlated with itself. But if $\bar{x}$ be the A_1 term correlated with the A-term x_1 we have: x_1 precedes x and therefore (correlates in A_1) $\bar{x}$ precedes x_1. Since $\bar{x}$ is not correlated with itself x_1 is not the first of its kind.

Cor. 1. *Two different sections of a* W *cannot be similar.*

For the less is a section of the greater.

Cor. 2. A W *cannot be similar to two different sections of another* W.

8. *Prop.* 6. *If* A_1, A_2 *are different sections of a* W A, B_1 *and* B_2 *similar sections of another,* B, *then* $B_1 \gtrless B_2$ *according as* $A_1 \gtrless A_2$.

Suppose $A_1 > A_2$, and that a is the element of A which determines the section A_2. Let b be the correspondent of a in the (unique) correlation $A_1 \sim B_1$. b has predecessors in B_1 (definition of similarity) and determines a section $B_2' < B_1$, similar to A_2. B_2 and B_2' are therefore similar sections of B, therefore identical. Hence $B_2 = B_2' < B_1$.

Prop. 7. *If in two* W's A *and* B *there is a similar section in* B *corresponding to every section of* A, *and vice versa, then* A ~ B.

With each a correlate the b which determines the (necessarily unique) section B_1 similar to A_1 determined by a, and *vice versa.*

---

* We may by now cut short the argument.

If b corresponds to a direct, a corresponds to b *vice versa*. (Prop. 5, Cor. 2.) By Prop. 6 the correlation is an ordinal one.

9. *Prop.* 8. *If two* W's A *and* B *are such that to every section of* A *corresponds a similar one of* B, *but not vice versa, then* A *is similar to a section of* B.

To every a, determining a section A', make correspond b, determining a similar section B'. The members of B are not exhausted; the remainder have a first, b_1 say. Then A and B_1 (determined by b_1) have the property of the hypothesis of Prop. 7, and are similar.

10. *Prop.* 9. *Given two* W's, A *and* B, (i) *either* (1) A $\sim$ B, *or* (2) *a section of* B, $B_1 \sim$ A, *or* (3) *a section of* A, $A_1 \sim$ B; (ii), (1), (2), (3) *are mutually exclusive.*

(i) There are four *a priori* possibilities.

  (a) To every section of A there corresponds a similar section in B, and *vice versa*.

  (b) To every section of A there corresponds a similar section in B, but not *vice versa*.

  (c) (b) with A and B interchanged.

  (d) A has a section to which no similar one in B corresponds, and *vice versa*.

In case (a) A $\sim$ B (Prop. 7).

In cases (b) and (c) A $\sim B_1$ and B $\sim A_1$ (Prop. 8).

Case (d) is impossible. For let A_1 be the least section of A having no similar section in B, B_1 the least section of B having no similar section in A. To every section A_2 of A_1 there is a similar section B_2 in B, which must be a section of B_1. (For it cannot be B_1 by the definition of B_1; and B_1 cannot be a section of B_2, for then B_1 would correspond to a section of A_2.) Similarly *vice versa*. Then $A_1 \sim B_1$ by Prop. 7, and this gives a contradiction.

Part (ii) follows by Prop. 5.

11. *Prop.* 10. *A part* B *of a* W A *is similar to* A *or to a section of* A.

We may suppose B a proper non-null part. If now the result of the theorem is false for A and B, A is similar (by a correlation R, say) to a section A′ of B (Prop. 9). Now B is a proper non-null part of A. Therefore B (*qua* part of A) corresponds by R to a *proper non-null part*, B′ say, of A′. If now B′ ∼ A′ or a section of A′, then B ∼ B′ ∼ A′ or a section of A′, therefore ∼ a section of B. This is impossible (Prop. 5), and it follows (Prop. 9) that A′ and its proper non-null part B′ have the same property as A and B. The process may be repeated, giving pairs A″, B″, ..., $A^{(n)}$, $B^{(n)}$, with the original property of A and B. Since A, B are never null the process cannot end. It yields therefore a descending progression of elements $a′$, $a″$, ... (determining A′, A″, ...), which is impossible (Prop. 3).

12. The *order-type* or *serial number* of *any* series is defined to be the class of all series (ordinally) similar to the given series. The order-type of a W is called an ordinal number.

The null-class and a unit-class (regarded as series——''honorary members''*) are said to have ordinals $\dot{0}$, $\dot{1}$ respectively.

Prop. 11. *Given two* W's, A *and* B, *of ordinals a and* β; *if* A *is not similar to* B, *but a section of* A *is similar to* B, *then any similar series* A′ *and* B′ *have the same property.*

For similarity is transitive, a section corresponds to a section in an ordinal correlation, and an ordinal correlation is unique.

Given α, β *there are* W's A *and* B *with* α, β *as ordinals. Definition. We say* α > β, β < α *if the relation of the hypothesis of Prop.* 11 *holds.* In virtue of *Prop.* 11 the definition is legitimate. Thus:

If α > β, *and* A *has ordinal* α, *there is one and only one section of* A *of ordinal* β.

---

* Strictly speaking a series must have at least two terms.

Prop. 12. (i) *Given two ordinals* α, β, *either* $\alpha > \beta$, *or* $\alpha = \beta$, *or* $\alpha < \beta$. *Also these relations are mutually exclusive.*

(ii) *If* $\alpha < \beta$ *and* $\beta < \gamma$, *then* $\alpha < \gamma$.

Thus "$<$" between ordinals satisfies the Axioms of Order.

(i) follows from Props. 11 and 9. (ii) is easy.

Addition. If we "place" a W of ordinal β "after" a W of ordinal α the result is a new W (ordered by certain obvious rules). With different representative series the new construction is ordinally similar to the first, so the ordinal depends only on α and β. This ordinal we define to be $\alpha + \beta$.

Multiplication. Given α, β, let A, B be W's of ordinals α and β. In place of each α place a W similar to B.* *It is easy to see that the result is a W.* Its ordinal is independent of the series used in the construction and its value is defined to be $\beta\alpha$.

It is easily seen that addition is associative, but not (necessarily) commutative, multiplication associative, distributive (in the form $\alpha(\beta + \gamma) = \alpha\beta + \alpha\gamma$), but not commutative. We shall not go into further details.

Since (Prop. 10) the ordinal of part of a W is less than or equal to the ordinal of the W, we have $\alpha + \beta \geqslant \beta$. But we do not necessarily have $\alpha + \beta > \beta\,(\beta > 0)$. We *do* have, however, $\alpha + \beta > \alpha\,(\beta > 0)$.

The Finite Ordinals.

13. *Prop.* 13. (i) *A class with finite cardinal n can be arranged as a W.* (ii) *If it is arranged as a series, the series is a W.* (iii) *Every W in which any class of given cardinal n can be arranged has the same ordinal.* (iv) *Every such W has a last term,* (v) *and every term but the first has an immediate predecessor.*

We prove (i), (ii) and (iv) *en bloc* by induction. They are true for $n = 2$ and may easily be verified in the conventional cases

---

* It can be shown easily that Mult. Ax. is not involved.

$n = 0, 1$. Assume them true for $n \leqslant N$, and consider them for $n \leqslant N + 1$. Let $C = C' + (x)$; C' has at most N terms.

(i) Arrange C' in a W and then put (x) at the beginning. This gives a W. (i) is true for $N + 1$.

(ii) Let C be arranged in a series; C_1 followed by (x) followed by C_2. C_1 and C_2 have cardinal at most N, therefore, by hypothesis, C_1 and C_2 are W's. Hence the series is a W.

(iv) In the W, $\{C_1, (x), C_2\}$, C_2, having at most N terms, has a last, or (if C_2 is absent) x is a last term of the W.

Hence (i), (ii), (iv) are true, generally, by induction.

(iii) Let W_1, W_2 be arrangements of C_1 and C_2, any two classes of cardinal n (perhaps identical). If W_1 is not similar to W_2 either $W_1 \sim$ (section of W_2), or *vice versa*. The ordinal correlation gives a cardinal correlation between C_1 and a proper part of C_2, and *vice versa*. This is impossible for finite classes of the same cardinal.

(v) If y is a term, not the first, of the W, the terms preceding it are a non-null sub-class of a finite class, therefore with a finite non-zero cardinal. By (iv) these terms have a last, which is an immediate predecessor of y.

Property (v) might be used to define finitude. But this requires us to introduce "order" from the first, and the conception is really irrelevant to the theory of cardinals.

Definition. The ordinal corresponding (uniquely) to the cardinal n in the light of Prop. 13 is denoted by $\dot{n}$. These ordinals are called finite. An infinite ordinal is one that is not finite.

14. *Prop. 14.* (i) $\dot{n} \gtreqqless \dot{m}$ *according as* $n \gtreqqless m$ *and conversely.* (ii) *There is exactly one distinct ordinal corresponding in the manner of the definition to each finite n.* (iii) $\dot{n} + \dot{m} = \overline{n + m}$ $= \overline{m + n} = \dot{m} + \dot{n}$, $\dot{n}\dot{m} = \overline{nm} = \overline{mn} = \dot{m}\dot{n}$, *and the arithmetic is the same as that of cardinals.*

Take W_1, W_2 of ordinals $\dot{n}$ and $\dot{m}$.

(i) If $\dot{n} > \dot{m}$, $W_2 \sim$ section of W_1; the class of W_2 is correlated (ordinally, therefore, cardinally) with a proper part of the class W_1. For finite classes this involves $n > m$. Similarly if $\dot{n} = \dot{m}$, $W_1 \sim W_2$ and $n = m$. This proves the converse. Also since one of the three relations $> = <$ holds between ordinals, the direct result follows also.

(ii) is already known, but is repeated for completeness.

(iii) The W corresponding to $\dot{n} + \dot{m}$ is $[W_1, W_2]$. This has $n + m$ terms. Hence $\dot{n} + \dot{m} = \overline{\dot{n + m}}$. But $n + m = m + n$. Similarly for multiplication.

15. Suppose we are given an infinite ordinal, or a corresponding W. Compare it with the $\dot{n}[\dot{1}, \dot{2}, \ldots, \dot{n}]$ which we will call B. B has n terms (Prop. F. 7 Cor.). If now A is ordinally similar to B or a section of B, then A is cardinally similar to B or a subclass of B, and is finite, which is false. Hence B is (ordinally) similar to a section of A (Prop. 9). Since an ordinal correlation is unique it follows that, for each n, the "nth term" of A exists. We deduce:

Prop. 15. An infinite W begins with a progression.

Cor. 1. An infinite ordinal exceeds $\dot{n}$ for every finite $\dot{n}$.

Cor. 2. A W in which every non-null sub-series has a last term is necessarily finite.

Prop. 16. The necessary and sufficient condition that α should be infinite is that $\dot{1} + \alpha = \alpha$. [N.B. $\alpha + \dot{1} > \alpha$ in any case.]

It is necessary by Prop. 15, since a progression remains a progression if a term is added at the beginning. It is sufficient since $\dot{1} + \dot{n} = \dot{n} + \dot{1} > \dot{n}$, so that α cannot be an $\dot{n}$.

16. *Prop. 17. The ordinals in order of magnitude form a W.*

They form a *series* (*Prop*. 12). We have to show that any class of distinct ordinals has a least member. Select any member α. If it is less than all others of the class there is nothing to prove. If not, consider the sub-class C of ordinals of the original class $< \alpha$. It is not null, and it is enough to show that it has a least member. Let A be a W of ordinal α. Given any β of C (necessarily $< \alpha$) there is a unique section of A of ordinal β, determined by element b say. To the β's of C correspond b's of A; the latter have a first member, and to it corresponds a least β of C.

17. Denote the W of ordinals (beginning with $\dot{0}$) by O.

Prop. 18. *The ordinal number of the section of O by the member α is α, or (alternatively) the ordinal of the W of β's such that $\beta < \alpha$ is α.*

This is true for $\dot{2}$, and also for $\dot{0}$, $\dot{1}$. If it is not always true, let β be the first ordinal for which it is not true, and let the section B determined by β have ordinal γ. If $\gamma < \beta$ the section of O by γ has ordinal γ (by the definition of β), and is therefore similar to the section by β, which is impossible by Prop. 5 Cor. 1. If $\gamma > \beta$ there is a section B_1 of B with ordinal β, the section being determined by δ say, $\delta < \beta$. But then by the definition of β this section has ordinal δ, again a contradiction.

Prop. 18 may be compared with Prop. F. 7. The latter leads to an infinity, of finite cardinals, the former, as we shall see, to the transfinite, of ordinals.

Meanwhile there are two important aspects of Prop. 18:

(i) the W of ordinals β such that $\beta < \alpha$ constitutes a "standard" W of ordinal α (much as the m satisfying $1 \leqslant m \leqslant n$ constitute a standard class of n terms).

(ii) a W of ordinal α can be "labelled off" as "(a_β) $(\beta < \alpha)$". [Compare §21, Chapter I.]

18. The arguments and theorems that follow are subject to later revision.

Prop. 19.   *Every class of ordinals in* O *has an immediate successor.*

For let A be the W consisting of every ordinal which is or precedes a member of the class, and let the ordinal of A be α. The section of O by α is A. Thus O never comes to any sort of end.

19. *The Alephs.*

ω and Ξ_0. Consider the W of finite ordinals. This is identical with the W of all β such that the section of O by β has a finite number of terms. (Also the β are the $\dot{n}$.) The ordinal of this W is defined as ω. ω is therefore the immediate successor of the W in O. The section of O by ω cannot have a finite number of terms, otherwise ω would be a β, whereas ω succeeds all β's. Thus ω is infinite. Further, any section of the W is a section by a β, i.e. an $\dot{n}$, therefore has a finite ordinal. Or, the same thing, any $\gamma < \omega$ is finite. Thus ω is the *least* infinite ordinal. ω is the ordinal of the progression $\dot{0}, \dot{1}, \dots$, therefore of all progressions. The cardinal of ω is Ξ_0.

ω_1 and Ξ_1. Consider the W of all ordinals β such that the section of O by β has Ξ_0 or a finite number of terms. The ordinal of this W, or what is the same thing, its immediate successor in O, is called ω_1. (It exists by *Prop.* 19.) The section of O by ω_1, i.e. the W of ordinals $\beta < \omega_1$, cannot have Ξ_0 or a finite number of terms, for then ω_1 would be a β. The cardinal, Ξ_1, of an ω_1, clearly $\geqslant \Xi_0$, is therefore $> \Xi_0$. Thus an ω_1 has Ξ_1 terms, and any section of it has Ξ_0 (or a finite number) of terms, and so *less* than Ξ_1 terms.

A *part* of an ω_1 has n, Ξ_0 or Ξ_1 terms. (For it is similar to the ω_1 or to a section of it.)

Similarly, by obvious definitions, we proceed to Ξ_2, Ξ_3, $\dots$ and ω_2, ω_3, $\dots$. Generally we have

Prop. 20.   *Corresponding to every ordinal* β *there is a unique ordinal* ω_β *and cardinal* Ξ_β *with the following properties. Let* A_β *be the* W *of all ordinals* γ *such that the cardinal of the section of* O *by* γ *(i.e. of the ordinals less than* γ*) is less than or* *equal to* Ξ_δ *for some* $\delta < \beta$; ω_β *and* Ξ_β *are the ordinals and cardinal of* A_β. *Moreover, if* $\beta > \beta'$, *then* $\omega_\beta > \omega_{\beta'}$ *and* $\Xi_\beta > \Xi_{\beta'}$.

[N.B.——The oddness of the enunciation and the proof is the price of avoiding "*definition* by transfinite induction" (to which, in point of fact, there is no logical objection).]

All this is true for $\beta = \dot{1}$. If all is not true for every β, let β be the first ordinal for which there is failure. Then Ξ_δ exists and is unique for every $\delta < \beta$, and so A_β exists and is unique. Let ω_β and Ξ_β be its (unique) ordinal and cardinal. Failure must therefore be due to the fact that there is some $\beta > \beta'$ for which $\omega_\beta > \omega_{\beta'}$ and $\Xi_\beta > \Xi_{\beta'}$ is false. But $A_{\beta'}$ is evidently a section of A_β, therefore $\omega_\beta > \omega_{\beta'}$. Further, $\Xi_\beta \geqslant \Xi_{\beta'}$. But if $\Xi_\beta = \Xi_{\beta'}$, ω_β (having cardinal $\Xi_{\beta'}$) is a γ, by definition, and therefore a member of A_β: an impossibility. Hence $\Xi_\beta > \Xi_{\beta'}$, and there turns out to be no failure after all.

20. *Prop. 21. If* $a < \Xi_\beta$ *then* a *is finite or an* Ξ_γ, *where* $\gamma < \beta$.

For a class of cardinal a is cardinally similar to part of an ω_β, therefore to the ω_β or a section of it. But a section of an ω_β has a cardinal $\leqslant \Xi_\gamma$, where $\gamma < \beta$. (Prop. 20——the ω_β is ordinally similar to A_β.) Hence $a \leqslant \Xi_\gamma$, since cardinal similarity to the ω_β implies $a = \Xi_\beta$. That is $a = \Xi_\gamma$ or $a < \Xi_\gamma$. In the latter case we repeat the argument, and so on. We get either a finite or $a = \Xi_\delta$ for some $\delta < \beta_1$ or else an infinite descending W of Ξ's, impossible by Prop. 3.

Cor. There is no $a < \Xi_\beta$ *such that* $a > \Xi_\gamma$ *for all* $\gamma < \beta$. *In particular there cannot be an* a *such that* $\Xi_\gamma < a < \Xi_{\gamma+i}$.

21. *Prop. 22. Given* β, *there is an* $\omega_\gamma \geqslant \beta$.

Consider the class of δ such that $\omega_\delta < \beta$ and let γ be the immediate successor of the class in O. Clearly $\omega_\gamma \geqslant \beta$.

Prop. 23. *The cardinal of any* $\mathbb{W}$ *is an aleph, or finite.*

For if β is its ordinal, $\beta \leqslant$ some ω_γ (Prop. 22). Therefore the $\mathbb{W}$ is ordinally similar to a section of an ω_γ or to the ω_γ, and so has cardinal $\leqslant \Xi_\gamma$. Apply Prop. 21.

22. *Burali-Forti's contradiction.* In Prop. 19 take the class to be O itself. We obtain a blank contradiction. This is historically the first of a number of contradictions, all of which arise by "mixing types", treating on the same footing entities of different logical type, e.g. a class and one of its members, the ordinal of a series of ordinals and an ordinal of the series concerned. (An account will be found in Russell's book). The remedy is to set up a hierarchy of types, the lowest, type 1, of "individuals", type 2 entities like classes of terms of type 1, and so on; and e.g. a "class" is not recognized as an entity unless its terms are all of the same type.

We need also an "axiom of infinity", that the number of individuals is infinite (it may amuse the reader to track down the precise place where we cheated). Granted this, the account we have given legitimately yields the finite ordinals $\dot{n}$. [It is interesting to note that this involves "constructing" an Ξ_0 out of a given infinity; the same thing is done in §32, Chapter I, by an apparently sophisticated argument; the reader may, however, verify on analysis that the two constructions are effectively the same!]. We now start with the set of $\dot{n}$ as raw material; they are of a certain type whose exact label need not trouble us, call it t. These ordinals $\dot{n}$ can be rearranged to give every possible order type of cardinal Ξ_0. The ordinals of these $\mathbb{W}$'s are of type $t + 2$; these *ordinals* form a $\mathbb{W}$ with terms of type $t + 2$. The ordinal of sections of this $\mathbb{W}$ are of type $t + 4$. The proof we gave of the existence of ω_1 and Ξ_1 applies, but in type $t + 4$. Similarly, having now Ξ_1 entities in type $t + 4$, we can arrange them to give every order type of cardinal Ξ_1, thus with a rise of type to $t + 8$ we get the existence of Ξ_2 and ω_2. In this way we can reach any finite type, but we cannot prove the existence of Ξ_ω or higher alephs. Similarly, we cannot prove the existence of any infinity of infinite cardinals. For, e.g. the step from a to 2^a by sub-classes involves a rise of type.

On the other hand we have proved, by implication, that *if* W's exist of sufficient "length" to give Ξ's up to some point, then the properties of our theorems hold for them. For the ordinals up to the point may be taken all of one type, and the consideration of the ordinals of a W of these ordinals involves only a single rise of type (a rise of 4).

[Prop. 18 is true in any case with *one* rise of type.]

23. *Prop.* 24. (*Hartogs' Theorem.*) *Any cardinal a is either an aleph (or finite) or incommensurable with all alephs from some Ξ_β onward.*

Let A be a class of cardinal a. Consider all W's that can be formed from the terms of A. Let γ (in *some* type) be the immediate successor of all the ordinals of these W's, and let B be a W of ordinal γ, Ξ_δ its cardinal.

Clearly A has no part cardinally similar to B. Hence $a \geqslant \Xi_\delta$ is false, i.e. $a < \Xi_\delta$ or a is incommensurable with Ξ_δ. In the first case a is an aleph (or finite) (Prop. 21). In the second a is incommensurable with Ξ_β for $\beta \geqslant \delta$. For if $a \geqslant \Xi_\beta$, then $a \geqslant \Xi_\delta$; and if $a < \Xi_\beta$ then a is an aleph, and so commensurable with Ξ_δ.

Cor. No cardinal is greater than all alephs.

Prop. 25. *Suppose there exists a selector-function f for the set of non-null sub-classes of a non-null class X. Then there exists an ordinal α, and a unique set*

$$(x_\beta) \ (1 \leqslant \beta < \alpha)$$

of distinct x's of X, such that

$$\sum_{\beta < \alpha} (x_\beta) = X, \quad x_\beta = f(X_\beta),$$

where $\qquad X_{\delta} = X, \ X_{\beta} = X - \sum_{\gamma < \beta} (x_{\gamma}) \ (\dot{0} < \beta < \alpha);$

incidentally X is well-ordered as (x_{β}) $(\beta < \alpha)$.

This is a transfinite analogue of Theorem 16, Chapter I, with the difference that the transfinite process exhausts X; the proof runs nearly parallel.

Let $\text{II}_{1,2}(\beta)$ be respectively the propositional functions:

"for each $\gamma \leqslant \beta^*$ there exists $\begin{cases} \text{at least} \\ \text{at most} \end{cases}$ one set $(x_{\gamma})(\gamma \leqslant \beta)$

of distinct x, for which

(1) $\quad x_{\gamma} = f(A_{\gamma})$, where $A_{\gamma} = A - \sum_{\delta < \gamma} (x_{\delta})$ is not null†".

$\text{II}_{1,2}$ are true for $\beta = \dot{1}$, and II_1 is true for smaller β if true for larger (A_{γ} is a "shrinking" set). Next, II_2 is always true, by transfinite induction, since if two sets agree for suffixes less than γ the two x_{γ}'s (if any) are f's of identical things and so identical. Let $\beta = \alpha$ be the first instance of failure# of $\text{II}_1(\beta)$. Then $x \varepsilon X$ for all $\gamma < \alpha$ and $\sum_{\gamma < \alpha} (x_{\gamma}) \subset A$. If now $A - \sum_{\gamma < \alpha}$ is not null it can figure as A_{α}, with its f as x_{α}, to give the existence of a set up to $\beta = \alpha$, with $\text{II}_1(\alpha)$ true. Hence $\sum_{\gamma < \alpha} (x_{\gamma}) = A$,

and the theorem is proved except for uniqueness of the set (x_{β}) $(\beta < \alpha)$. But there cannot be two different sets, for if they differed at suffix β this would contradict $\text{II}_2(\beta)$.

24. *Mult. Ax. and Well-ordered Series.*

(1) *Mult. Ax.* $\equiv$. *Any class can be well ordered* $(= \mathbb{W})$.**

* Note it is $\gamma \leqslant \beta$, not $\gamma < \beta$ (but $\delta < \gamma$ below).
† This of course includes $\sum_{\delta < \gamma}$ being contained in A.
# This may involve a rise of type if $\text{II}_1(\beta)$ is true for all β of the original one; but only one rise since there are no x_{β} in the higher type.
[The truth of $\text{II}_2(\beta)$ survives the rise of type, owing to its negative character.]
** $p \equiv q$, where p and q are propositions, means "p is equivalent to q", or that both p implies q and q implies p.

(i) Assuming Mult. Ax. there is a selector-function for any class A, and by Theorem 25 A can be well-ordered.

(ii) If every class can be well-ordered, then, given a class of existent classes B, we well-order their *sum*. We can select the first member of each B, and the M.C. is not null.

(2) *Mult. Ax.* $\equiv$ *"every cardinal is an aleph"* ($=$ A). For W implies **A**, by Prop. 23; also A implies **W**. Hence **A** $\equiv$ **W** $\equiv$ Mult. Ax.

(3) *Mult. Ax.* $\equiv$ *Trichotomy** ($=$ T).

Mult. Ax. implies **A**, and therefore **T**; also **T** and Prop. 24 imply **A**.

(4) *If Mult. Ax. is true, then* ω_1 *is not the immediate successor of an ascending progression* β_1, β_2, ... *of ordinals.*

For if ω_1 is such an immediate successor, $\beta_n < \omega_1$. The sections of O by β_n, β_{n+1} being denumerable, the class A_n of β such that $\beta_n < \beta \leqslant \beta_{n+1}$, is denumerable. We now have $\underset{n}{\Sigma A_n}$ denumerable, *by Mult. Ax.* [(1), *Cor.* of I, §39.] But by hypothesis the sum class consists of all ordinals less than ω_1.

(5) To end, we digress to mention, with an indication of the proof, a result with many applications in advanced theory. If Mult. Ax. is true, or with the more limited assumption that the continuum of real numbers x can be well-ordered, *there exists a 'basis' for the real numbers, that is a set of real numbers* ξ *such that every* x *except* 0 *is expressible uniquely as a finite sum* $\Sigma r \xi$, *where the coefficients* r *are rational.*

Suppose the x arranged as a W: the ξ are determined (as a subseries of W) as follows. Given a class of real numbers typified by θ, φ, ..., we denote by $[\theta, \varphi, ...]$ the class of non-zero x expressible by finite sums of type $\Sigma r \theta$. Take $\xi_1 = 1$. Take ξ_2 to be the first x in W not in $[\xi_1]$, ξ_3, the first x not in $[\xi_1, \xi_2]$ (which includes $[\xi_1]$), ..., and generally ξ_α to be the first x not in $[(\xi_\beta) (1 \leqslant \beta < \alpha)]$.

---

*I.e. the proposition that one of the relations $=$, $>$, $<$ holds between any pair of cardinals.

An application (for the reader acquainted with Lebesgue measure) is a proof of the existence of non-measureable sets (there exists no such proof without some assumption). Let E be the part of the set $[\xi_\beta (\beta > 1)]$ contained in $0 < x < 1$, E_n the set $E + r_n$, where (r_n) is a denumeration of the rationals in $0 < r < 1$. E_1, E_2, ... are mutually exclusive and all lie in $0 < x < 2$. Since each E_n is a translation of E, they all have the same measure, if any. This measure cannot be positive, and it cannot be 0 since in the theory of measure the sum set of a denumerable class of sets of zero measure has zero measure. (This theorem, incidentally, involves an appeal to the principle that the sum class of a denumerable class of denumerable classes is denumerable, which is not provable, even in the rather special case concerned, without assumption.)

25. There is a result, independent of any assumption, in the opposite direction to (4).

Prop. 26. If $\gamma < \omega_1$, there is an ascending progression of ordinals of which γ is the sequent, or γ has an immediate predecessor.

Arrange the class of β's less than γ in a progression (δ_1, δ_2, ...). Let $\beta_1 = \delta_1$. Let

β_2 = the δ of least suffix n_2 for which $\delta > \beta_1$,

β_3 = the δ of least suffix n_3 greater than n_2 for which
$$\delta > \delta_1, \delta_2, ..., \delta_{n_2},$$

β_4 = the δ of least suffix n_4 greater than n_3 for which
$$\delta > \delta_1, \delta_2, ..., \delta_{n_3},$$

and so on. This process can terminate, at β_m say, only if γ is the immediate successor of δ_1, δ_2, ..., δ_{n_m} (otherwise β_{m+1} will exist). In this case γ has an immediate predecessor. In the other case we have an ascending progression (β_n); let γ' be its immediate successor. Clearly $\gamma' \leqslant \gamma$. If $\gamma' < \gamma$ we have $\gamma' = \delta_p$ say. Since n_r tends to ∞ with r, we have $n_r > p (r > r_0)$, and $\beta_{r+1} > \delta_1$, δ_2, ..., δ_{n_r}, $\beta_{r+1} > \delta_p = \gamma'$. This is impossible, and so $\gamma' = \gamma$.

CHAPTER III.

Other Types of Series

1. In what follows we consider series of arbitrary type. We write "<" for the ordering relation "precedes". We use it also, in the obvious way, to mean "precedes" between two parts (subseries) if all terms of the one precede all terms of the other.

A series S is called bounded if it has a first and a last term, unbounded if it has neither a first nor a last term.

Sections of an S. These are direct generalizations of Dedekind sections of the series of rationals (which create the series of real numbers). Suppose L, R are sub-series of S, with l, r respectively typical terms, and with the properties: (1) L + R contains all the terms of S, (2) any pair l, r satisfy $l < r$. Then L is called a section of S.* L or R can be null; the section is called "proper" if R is not null.

There are 4 possibilities for a section: (i) L has a last term, R a first; (ii) L has a last, R no first; (iii) L has no last, R has a first; (iv) L has no last, R no first. In (i) the section is said to have a "jump"; in (ii) and in (iii) to be a "cut", or be "continuous"; in (iv) to have a "gap".

We note two specially important kinds of section, S_x, the series of terms y preceding x, and S_{x+}, which is S_x followed by the term x. (W's are characterised by the fact that every proper section is an S_x. For simplicity we used "section" (of a W) in Chapter II to mean what we now call a proper section.) In an ordinal correlation all these things correspond in the obvious ways.

* We define the section to be L, the thing cut off, not, as we might, the o.p. (L, R), which is a making precise of the "act of cutting". As a matter of linguistics, both "Schnitt" and "section" are ambiguous in this way.

2. A series S is called dense if no section has a jump; an equivalent (perhaps more familiar) definition is that between any two distinct terms there is another (and so an infinity of others).

A *bounded* S is called "closed" if no section has a gap, "continuous" if no section has either gap or jump.

If a bounded S is continuous every section is either an S_x or an S_{x+}. The S_x, or again the S_{x+}, are further such that of any two different ones one is a section, of corresponding type, of the other, and may be said to "precede" it. This gives rise to a new series, the series of S_x (S_{x+}). Either of them is similar to the original continuous S.[†]

If S is dense[‡] (but not necessarily continuous), consider the class of all sections[§] L in which L is "open", i.e. has no last term. Of two L's one is a section of the other, and this relation yields a new series $\hat{S}$ whose elements are L's. We call it the "completion" of S.

Prop. 1.   *The completion $\hat{S}$ of a dense S is continuous.*

Prop. 2.   *The completions $\hat{S}$ of similar S (of any type) are similar.*

(1) We have to deal with two ordering relations, of S and $\hat{S}$. For clarity we keep the symbol "<" for the ordering relation of S (using it also, as explained, between sub-series when one precedes another). The ordering relation of $\hat{S}$ does not occur till near the end, we will call it "$\lessdot$".

Consider a section $\mathcal{L}$ of $\hat{S}$, with its complementary $\mathcal{R}$ ($\mathcal{L}$ and $\mathcal{R}$ have L's for members). There is no jump: L and L′ must have L's between them since S is dense. [One of L, L′, say L′, has a term x not in L; being open L′ has an $x' > x$, when $S_{x'}$ is an L between L, L′.]

Let L_1, L_2 be typical members of $\mathcal{L}$, $\mathcal{R}$, R_1, R_2 their complements S-L_1, S-L_2, (suffix 1 associated with $\mathcal{L}$, 2 with $\mathcal{R}$): it re-

---

[†]Strictly speaking this is "mixing logical types", but it is a trivial matter to rectify.

[‡]No restriction of bounded or unbounded.

[§]Including those for which L is null or R is null.

mains to prove that there is not a gap, that is, to produce either a first L_1 or a last L_2.

Let $L^* = \Sigma L_1$, $R^* = \Pi R_1 = \Pi(S-L_1)$. Then†

(i) $R^* = S-\Sigma L_1$, or $L^* + R^* = S$;

(ii) $L^* < R^*$, since a term of L^* is a term of some L_1, so $<R_1 \leqslant \Pi R_1 = R^*$;

(iii) L^* is open, since a last term of it would be the last of some L_1.

(i), (ii) and (iii) show that L^* is a section of S with L^* open, i.e. L^* *is an* L. Now from $L_1 \lessdot L_2$ it follows that $L^* \lessdot L_2$; and since (trivially) $L_1 \lesssim L^*$, we have, for all L_1, L_2,

$$L_1 \lesssim L^* \lessapprox L_2.$$

So L^*, being either an L_1 or an L_2, is the last of $\mathcal{L}$ or the first of $\mathcal{R}$, as desired. This completes the proof of Prop. 1.

Prop. 2 is immediate from the invariance of section, jump, gap, etc. in an ordinal correlation.

4. *Prop. 3. A bounded continuous* S *is similar to the completion of any subseries* D *of* S *dense in* S. [*In particular the order-type of such an* S *is unaltered by completion.*]

That D is dense in S means that between two different *s* there is a *d*.

Use suffixes S, D to denote sections of S or D.

Given any open L_S, associate with it the L_D composed of the terms of D preceding R_S; this L_D is open. To different L_S different L_D correspond (there are *d*'s, between the two L_S); also a given L_D is associated with that L_S, determined by L_D, whose members are the terms of S each preceding some member of L_D. The correspondence of the L_D with the L_S is therefore one-one, and it is ordinal. So $\mathcal{D} \sim \mathcal{S} \sim S$.

† (ii) of §2, Chapter I again.

The types of R *and* X.

5. R denotes the series of rationals between 0 and 1, both exclusive, in natural order. Its order-type is called η. X denotes the series of real numbers x satisfying $0 \leqslant x \leqslant 1$, in natural order. Its order-type is called θ.

Prop. 4. *The necessary and sufficient conditions that a series* S *is an* η *are*: (1) S *has* Ξ_0 *terms*; (2) S *is unbounded and dense.*

The necessity is obvious, since (1), (2) are invariant under ordinal correlation and are satisfied by R. ("Natural order" means: by the relation "<" between rationals, which clearly obeys the order axioms. Similarly later for X.) We shall prove sufficiency. By (1) S and R are each cardinally similar to an ω, and can be arranged as

$$S_0(s_1, s_2, \ldots),$$
$$R_0(r_1, r_2, \ldots).$$

Let $s^1 = s_1$, $r^1 = r_1$.
Let s^2 be the s of least suffix not so far taken (i.e. s_2). Let r^2 be the r of least suffix that is related to r_1 as s^2 to s^1 (i.e. r^2 succeeds or precedes r^1 according as s^2 succeeds or precedes s^1).

Let r^3 be the r of least suffix not so far taken.

Let s^3 be the s of least suffix not so far taken that is related to s^1, s^2 as r^3 is to r^1, r^2 (e.g. is between s^1, s^2 if r^3 is between r^1, r^2).

Let s^4 be the s of least suffix not so far taken.
And so on.[†] The rule determines two progressions of distinct terms, (s^n), (r^n), and the correlation $s^n \sim r^n$ is ordinal. (A full proof would be by induction, and though it is rather an elaborate one the reader has now seen enough of them to take it for granted.) Also, on account of the alternation of choice $(s, s, r, r, \ldots$ in-

[†] The choices are always possible since S and R are unbounded and dense.

stead of s, r, s, r, ...) the terms s and r are exhausted.[1] A full proof again requires rather an elaborate induction; this time we will compromise by indicating the nature of the $P(n)$ that the induction operates on.

"For each $m \leqslant n$ there exist sets of distinct terms $R_m = (r^1, r^2, ..., r^m)$, $S_m = (s^1, s^2, ..., s^m)$. R_m, S_m are obtained from R_{m-1}, S_{m-1} by addition of r^m, s^m in accordance with "the rule", and finally the correlation by indices between R_m and S_m (for $m \leqslant n$) is ordinal."

N.B.——There are many ordinal correlations between S and R.

Examples of η's. The positive and negative rationals in natural order. The rationals between a and b exclusive, or the real algebraic numbers, or those between a and b exclusive, in each case in natural order. [The rationals between 0 and 1 *inclusive* are of type $\dot{1} + \eta + \dot{1}$.]

6. *Prop.* 5. *Given any series* S *of* E_0 *terms, and an* η, E, *there is a sub-series of* E *similar to* S.

Arrange S as an ω, $S_0 = (s_1, s_2, ...)$, and E as $E_0 = (e_1, e_2, ...)$. Let $\varepsilon_1 = e_1$;

$\varepsilon_2 = $ the e of least suffix in E_0 related to ε_1 as s_2 to s_1;

$\varepsilon_3 = $ the e of least suffix in E_0 related to ε_1 and ε_2 as s_3 to s_1 and s_2;

and so on. (Each ε exists since E is unbounded and dense.) The class of ε's (ordered as in E) has the required property.

Lemma. *Given any ordinal* $\beta < \omega_1$, *there is a class of rationals which, in order of magnitude, form a* $\mathbb{W}$ *of ordinal* β.

This is an immediate corollary.

7. *Prop.* 6. *The continuum* $0 \leqslant x \leqslant 1$ *contains* $\bar{\mathrm{E}}_1$ *mutually exclusive non-null sets of points* (Lebesgue).

[1] This happy idea evades the formidable complications of the original proof, which used s, r, s, r, ...

Cor. $2^c \geqslant 2^{\Xi_1} > \Xi_1$.

Arrange the rationals in an ω, $R_0 = (r_1, r_2, \ldots)$. For any x of $0 < x \leqslant 1$, $x = 2^{-n_1} + 2^{-n_2} + \ldots$, where $n_1, n_2, \ldots$ are a strictly increasing *infinite* series of positive integers. The representation is unique.

If $(r_{n_1}, r_{n_2}, \ldots)$ is, *in order of magnitude*, a W of ordinal β (naturally a very exceptional event), we assign x to the class E_β. The E_β are clearly mutually exclusive. Further, if $\omega \leqslant \beta < \omega_1$, E_β is not null. For there is a class C_β of rationals which, in natural order, forms a W of ordinal β. Let this class, ordered by increasing suffixes in R_0, be $(r_{n_1}, r_{n_2}, \ldots)$. This new series is not finite since the cardinal of C_β is Ξ_0 (not finite). Hence $2^{-n_1} + 2^{-n_2} + \ldots$ is an infinite series and the corresponding x belongs to E_β. Thus the continuum contains E_β for $\omega \leqslant \beta < \omega_1$, and the number of E's is Ξ_1.

The corollary follows by the lemma of I, §30.

8. *Prop. 7.* *If a bounded S* (i) *is continuous,* (ii) *contains a sub-series of* Ξ_0 *terms dense in S, it is similar to the continuum* $0 \leqslant x \leqslant 1$ *in natural order.*

Cor. (i) *and* (ii) *are necessary and sufficient conditions for a bounded S to be similar to the continuum* $0 \leqslant x \leqslant 1$.

The sub-series, less its first or last terms if any, is similar to R, by Prop. 4; by Prop. 2 the completions, which are respectively S and X, are similar. For the Corollary we need only observe that the conditions are invariant under ordinal correlation and that X satisfies them.

9. *Assuming Mult. Ax.*: (1) *any dense S contains a sub-series of type* η; (2) *any continuous S contains a sub-series of type* θ.

(1) We select, successively*; (i) s_1, s_2 following s_1; (ii) s_3 preceding s_1, s_4 between s_1 and s_2, s_5 following s_2; (iii) s_6 pre-

* The reader should make a diagram.

ceding s_3, s_7 between s_3 and s_1, s_8 between s_1 and s_4, s_9 between s_4 and s_2, s_{10} between s_2 and s_5, s_{11} following s_5; and so on. The selections are possible since we have a selector function for any class of S's.

In (2) S is dense, and contains an η by (1). So $\overset{\circ}{\delta}$ contains the completion of η; but $\overset{\circ}{\delta}$ is similar to S and the completion of the η is a θ.

These results (subject to the assumption) show that R is the thinnest possible dense series, and X the thinnest possible continuous one.

It is the case, without any assumption, that series exist that are much thicker than X. X is (roughly, ignoring double representation) the class of binary decimals in order of magnitude; that is, the class of words of type ω formed from an alphabet of two letters 0, 1, and arranged in "alphabetical order". If we take the same alphabet but make the words have type say ω_1, we obtain a much richer series.

CHAPTER IV.

Elements of the Theory of Sets of Points

1. A point (in space of n dimensions) is an ordered n-set of real numbers $(x_1, x_2, \ldots, x_n)$. A class of such points is called a *set*. A *bounded* set is a set for which there exists a common upper bound for all $|x_1|$, $|x_2|$, $\ldots$, $|x_n|$ of the set.

The distance pq between p, $(x_1, \ldots, x_n)$ and q, $(x_1', \ldots, x_n')$ is defined to be the real number $\sqrt{\{(x_1 - x_1')^2 + \ldots + (x_n - x_n')^2\}}$. "Cauchy's inequality" shows that $pq + qr \geqslant pr$. The *distance* $d(p, E)$ *between a point p and a set* E is defined to be the lower bound of pq for all q of E. The *distance* $d(E_1, E_2)$ *between a set* E_1 *and a set* E_2 is defined to be the lower bound of all $p_1 p_2$, p_1 belonging to E_1 and p_2 to E_2.

The *complementary set* of a given set is the set of points not belonging to the given set. We denote the complementary of E by CE.

Limit-point. There are two conceptions relating to a set E, which cannot be proved to be equivalent without Mult. Ax.; the first is that of a point p such that a progression of distinct points p_1, p_2, $\ldots$ of E exists for which pp_n tends to zero; the second is that of a point p such that in any neighbourhood (set of points q such that $qp < \delta$) of p there exists a point (therefore an infinity of points) of E other than p. It is (perhaps unexpectedly) the latter conception that is important; we call p a limit-point of E.

The *derived set* E' of E is the set of limit-points of E.

An *isolated point of* E is a point p of E that is not a limit-point; it is contained in a sphere of centre p containing no point of E other than p. A set E is called *dense-in-itself* if every point of E is a limit-point of E: i.e. if $E \subset E'$.

An *interior point p of* E is a point whose distance from CE is greater than 0; there exists a sphere with centre p all of whose points are points of E. An *exterior point of* E is a point whose distance from E is greater than 0. An exterior point of E is an interior point of CE and *vice versa*. A *frontier point p of* E is a point that is neither an exterior nor an interior point of E. It is also a frontier point of CE. (An isolated point is a frontier point.) A necessary and sufficient condition for p to be a frontier point is that any sphere of centre p contains at least one point of E and at least one point of CE.

The *characteristic function* φ of E is the function that takes the value 1 at points of E and the value 0 at other points. φ is continuous at exterior and interior points, and discontinuous at frontier points of E.

Prop. 1. *A set contained in a "rectangle", but not containing every point of the rectangle, has at least one frontier point in the rectangle.*

Let p be a point of the set, q a point not of the set, both in the rectangle. Consider the behaviour of φ on the "straight line" pq. The co-ordinates are continuous functions of t, the distance of the point from p, and $\varphi = \psi(t)$. ψ is 1 at p and 0 at q. It is therefore discontinuous at some point r in pq, otherwise it would take somewhere the value ½. φ is discontinuous at r, or ψ would *a fortiori* be continuous. Hence r is a frontier point.

2. *A set is called closed if it contains all its limit-points*; i.e. *if* $E' \subset E$. *A set is called open if every point is an interior point.* We use the symbols F and O for closed and open sets respectively. Closed and open sets are complementary; a CF is an O, a CO is an F.

Prop. 2. *A derived set* E' *is closed.*

We have to show that if p'' is a limit point of E' then it is one of E. Given any δ there exists a p' of E' within δ of p'', and *two* points p of E within δ of p', therefore one point p of E within 2δ of p'', where $p \neq p''$.

A *perfect set* is a non-null set which is closed and dense-in-itself, i.e. such that $E' = E$.

3. *Prop.* 3. *A sum ΣO of open sets is open, a product ΠF of closed sets is closed.*

The first is evident, since an interior point of a part is one of the whole. The second follows by the consideration of complementary sets.

Prop. 4. *The sum or product of a finite number of open or closed sets is open or closed.*

The results for closed sets are evident, those for open sets follow by taking complementaries.

4. *Prop.* 5. (*The generalised Borel theorem.*) *Given a bounded (closed) F, and a set of (open) O_p, one for each p of F, and each O_p containing p. Then F is contained in the sum of a finite number of the O_p.*

We use the bisection argument. If the result is false we get a nest of "squares" S each containing (when taken closed) points of F, and converging to a point π belonging to each S, such that each SF does not have the property of the theorem. But π is evidently a limit point of F, therefore a point of F, therefore interior to O_π, which consequently contains S's of the nest. This gives a contradiction.

Cor. 1. *If a product ΠF is contained in an O then a finite sub-product is contained in it.*

Cor. 2. *Two bounded (closed) sets F_1, F_2, with no common point, have a positive distance.*

Cor. 3. *Suppose F_n is a contracting sequence, more generally F_β ($\beta < \alpha$) a contracting series, of closed bounded non-null sets. Then their common part is not null.*

Cor. 1 is the complementary of the main theorem.

In *Cor.* 2 let $F_1(n)$ be the set of those points where distance d_n from F_1 satisfies $d_n \leqslant n^{-1}$. This is easily seen to be closed [if l is a limit point of $F_1(n)$ there is a p of $F_1(n)$ with $pl < \varepsilon$; p is within a distance $n^{-1} + \varepsilon$ from some q of F, and so $lq < n^{-1} + 2\varepsilon$; since ε is arbitrarily small $d(l, F_1) \leqslant n^{-1}$, so that l belongs to $F_1(n)$.] Any point not belonging to F_1 is a positive distance from F_1; hence $F_1 = \prod\limits_{n=1}^{\infty} F_1(n)$. On the other hand $F_1 \subset CF_2$, so $\amalg F_1(n) \subset CF_2$. The right hand side being an O, some finite product, with greatest $n = \nu$, say, is contained in CF_2, and then $d(F_1, F_2) \geqslant \nu^{-1}$.

In *Cor.* 3 all the F's are interior to some closed sphere S. Suppose that the common part is null. If p is any point of S p does not belong to all F_β, and so does belong to some CF_β, which is open. Hence the closed S is contained in a finite sum of CF_β's, and so in that CF_β of the sum with smallest suffix: this requires F_β to be null, contrary to hypothesis.

5. *Prop. 7. If in a bounded "rectangle" there are* (a) *an infinity of points, or* (b) *at least* Ξ_0 *points, or* (c) *exactly* Ξ_0 *points, or* (d) *a non-denumerable set of points, then there is a point ξ of the "rectangle" such that any rectangle including ξ has (respectively) the same property.*

We employ the bisection method. The proof turns on the facts that in cases (a) to (d); (1) if a "rectangle" has the property and is "quadrisected", one of its portions* has the property, (2) if a sub-rectangle has the property the whole rectangle has the property. (If we take the property of containing c points we cannot prove the corresponding (1) without Mult. Ax.)

Cor. In case (a) *there exists at least one limit point of the set.*

6. *A point of condensation* of E is a point in any neighbourhood of which there is a non-denumerable set of points of E.

───────

* Taken closed.

Prop. 8. *A bounded non-denumerable set* E *has at least one point of condensation.*

The existence of a point of condensation follows by Prop. 7 (d).

Prop. 8 (a). *Assuming Mult. Ax. we may omit* "*bounded*" *in the enunciation of Prop.* 8.

For an unbounded set is the sum of Ξ_0 bounded sets, and all of these cannot be denumerable if the whole set is not.

7. *Prop.* 9. *The set* K *of points of condensation of* E *is closed.*

A limit point p of K has, within any distance δ, a point of K, and therefore, within 2δ, a non-denumerable set of points of E; therefore p is a point of K.

Lemma. On Mult. Ax.*, *if* S *is the set of* p *of* E *for which* $d(p, \mathrm{K}) \geqslant \delta > 0$, *then* S *is denumerable.*

For if not, S has a point of condensation q (Prop. 8a), so that q belongs to K. But there are points p of S arbitrarily near q, and so with $d(p, \mathrm{K}) \leqslant pq < \delta$.

Prop. 10. *Assuming Mult. Ax., if* E *is closed then* (i) E − K *is denumerable*; (ii) K, *if not null, is perfect.*

If E is closed it contains K. (i) Let E_n be the set of points whose distance from K exceeds $1/(n + 1)$, but not $1/n$. Each E_n is denumerable by the lemma. Hence, on Mult. Ax., $\sum_n E_n$ is denumerable. But since K is closed any point of E − K has a positive distance from K and so belongs to $\sum E_n$. (ii) If p is an isolated point of K, and S is a sphere round it containing no other point of K, the set SE − (p) is contained in E − K, and is denumerable by (i). So p cannot be a point of K.

A Corollary of Prop. 10 is that, *assuming Mult. Ax., a closed set can be dissected into a denumerable set and a set perfect or*

---

* Mult. Ax. is required here only if E is unbounded.

null, the latter set being the set of points of condensation. Actually this proposition can be proved without Mult. Ax., but on entirely different lines. We make a fresh start.

8. *A scattered set*, or as we shall say for brevity, *a C-set, or a C, is a set which contains no sub-set dense-in-itself.*

Lemma.   A sub-set of a C is a C.

Prop. 11.   *Any set* E *is a* C *or the sum of a* C *and a set* H *dense-in-itself.*

This is obvious if E is a C. If not it contains some D sub-set, where we write for brevity D for "dense-in-itself". Let H be the sum of all such sub-sets. Then H is D. [Any point p of H belongs to some D sub-set of E, therefore is a limit point of this sub-set, therefore a limit point of H.] The remaining set clearly contains no D sub-set, and is a C.

Prop. 12.   H *is closed if* E *is.*

Since $H \subset H'$ a point of H', being a limit point of H, is *a fortiori* a limit point of H'; so H' is D. Since $H' \subset E$ if E is closed we have $H' \subset H$; H is closed.

9. We recall that there is a standard denumeration S_1, S_2, ... of the totality of rational spheres (I, Prop. 28).

Prop. 13.   *There exist three functions,* $p(C)$, $n(C)$, $S(C)$, *each with the same argument class* $\hat{a}$ *consisting of all non-null* C; $p(C)$ *is a point* p *of* C; $S(C)$ *contains* p *and no other point of* C *and is the* S *of least suffix* N *in the denumeration that contains exactly one point of* C; $S(C)$ *is* S_N; $n(C) = N$.

Since C has isolated points (else it would be D) there exist S_m that contain exactly one point of C. The S_m of least suffix N does all that is required.

Prop. 14.   *Any C-set is denumerable.*

$p(C)$ is a selector-function for the class of non-null C's. By Prop. 25, Chapter II, there is an α such that

$$C = \sum_{\beta < \alpha} (p_\beta), \quad C_0 = C, \quad C_\beta = C - \sum_{\gamma < \beta}(p_\gamma)$$

where $p_\beta = p(C_\beta)$. Since (for $\beta < \alpha$) $S(C_\beta)$ contains a point, p_β, absent from C_δ with $\delta > \beta$, the $S(C_\beta)$ are all different. Hence the $n(C_\beta)$ with $\beta < \alpha$ are all different, and the β (and p_β) must be denumerable.

Suppose now that E is a closed set, then so is H, by the Lemma. Since H is also **D** or null it is perfect or null. Hence we have:

Prop. 15. A closed set is the sum of a denumerable set, and the set H(E), perfect or null.

N.B.——We have not yet shown that the dissection $E = P + D$ is unique, nor that P is the set of points of condensation.

10. *The transfinite series of derived sets.* We suppose E closed (if not, E' is). We define

$$\text{(i) } E^{(n+1)} = (E^{(n)})'; \quad \text{(ii) } E^{(\omega)} = \prod_{n < \omega} (E^{(n)}).$$

By an extension of these processes we can define $E^{(\beta)}$ for any ordinal β. ($E^{(\beta)}$ may of course be null.) For if we have defined $E^{(\beta)}$ for all $\beta < \gamma$ we define $E^{(\gamma)}$ as $(E^{(\gamma')})'$ if γ has an immediate predecessor γ', and as $\prod_{\beta < \gamma} (E^{(\beta)})$ if it has none.

Prop. 16. Each $E^{(\beta)}$ is contained in all preceding ones, is closed, and contains the H of E.

All is true for $\beta = 1$. Assume all true for $\beta < \gamma$. Observe that then, since H is contained in $E^{(\beta)}$, H is the H of $E^{(\beta)}$, by the definition. There are two cases.

(1) $\gamma = \gamma' + 1$. By hypothesis $E^{(\gamma')}$ is closed, therefore contains $(E^{\gamma'})' = E^{(\gamma)}$. Further, $E^{(\gamma)}$ is closed, as a first de-

rived set. Finally, since $H(E_1)$ is contained in E_1', for any E_1, $H = H(E^{(\gamma')})$ is contained in $E^{(\gamma)}$.

(2) γ *has no immediate predecessor*. Then if $\alpha < \gamma$, $E^{(\gamma)}$ $= \amalg E^{(\beta)}$ is contained in $E^{(\alpha)}$. Further, $E^{(\gamma)}$ is closed as a product of closed sets. Finally, H is contained in $E^{(\beta)}(\beta < \gamma)$, and so H is contained in $\amalg E^{(\beta)} = E^{(\gamma)}$.

In either case all the properties are true for γ; they are therefore true generally by transfinite induction.

Prop. 17. *If E is closed there is a* $\beta < \omega_1$, *such that* $E^{(\beta)}$ $= E^{(\beta+i)}$, *so that* $E^{(\beta)}$ *is perfect or null*.

Evidently if any β has this property all subsequent ones have. If the Prop. is false $E^{(\beta)} - E^{(\beta+i)}$ is non-null for every $\beta < \omega_1$. But a point of the H of E belongs to every $E^{(\beta)}$; hence $E^{(\beta)}$ $- E^{(\beta+i)}$ is contained in C. Thus the $E^{(\beta)} - E^{(\beta+i)}$ for $\beta < \omega_1$ are exclusive* scattered sets, and the $p(E^{(\beta)} - E^{(\beta+i)})$ are Ξ_1 distinct points of C, which is impossible.

Cor. $E^{(\beta)} = H$.

For H is contained in $E^{(\beta)}$. Also, since $E^{(\beta)}$ is perfect, it is **D**, so that $E^{(\beta)}$ is contained in H.

The structure of open and closed linear sets.

11. *Linear* (1-*dimensional*) *sets*.

Prop. 18. *An open linear set O is a sum of a denumerable set of open non-overlapping intervals, and conversely*.

Any point of O is interior to O; hence associated with any p of O there is a greatest interval containing p and having as interior point no point of CO. [Its existence is proved by Dedekind section.] The ends of this interval are frontier points of O. Consider the class of all such distinct intervals. It is a non-overlap-

* Since $E^{(\beta)}$ is contained in $E^{(\gamma)}(\beta > \gamma)$.

ping set, therefore denumerable. Moreover, the set of intervals, taken open, clearly contains every point of O. Further, any point of one of the set is a point of O.

The converse is a special case of Prop. 3.

A closed linear set is the complement of a set of intervals. The intervals are called the black intervals of the set. Isolated points correspond to abutting black intervals.

The structure of a perfect set is given by the fact that no two black intervals abut.

12. *Linear perfect nowhere-dense sets* (L.P.N.D. sets). A linear set is said to be *dense* if between every two points of E there is a point of E. It is said to be nowhere dense if there is no interval in which the set is dense.

Evidently: *A necessary and sufficient condition for a perfect linear set* E *to be nowhere dense is that* E *should contain no interval*; or, again, *that between any two points of* E *there are black intervals of* E.

Prop. 20. *The series whose terms are* (a) *the points of a bounded* L.P.N.D. *set, with the exception of the end points of the black intervals, and* (b) *the black intervals qua single terms, is, taken in "natural" order, of type* θ. *Any two such series are ordinally similar, black intervals corresponding to black intervals.*

The black intervals are an Ξ_0 dense in S. If L is any non-null section of S, take the upper bound of right hand end points of black intervals of L. This is either the left hand end of a black interval, which is then the first term of R, or else a "white" point, which must be either the last term of L or the first of R. The conditions (i), (ii) of Prop. 7, Chapter III are accordingly satisfied.

Cor. 1. *Any two bounded, or two unbounded,* L.P.N.D. *sets are ordinally similar (in natural order).*

Cor. 2. *A perfect linear set has cardinal c.*

(i) The set bounded. If it is *not* N.D. it contains an interval; if it *is* it differs from a certain series of type θ only in the respect of Ξ_0 terms.

(ii) The set unbounded. The sub-set between two distinct black intervals is perfect and bounded, and contains c points, by (i).

13. *Extensions to non-linear sets.*

Lemma. If P *is a perfect set and* R *a (closed) rectangle with (some) points of* P *as interior points, then* RP *contains a perfect set.*

[N.B. The product of two perfect sets need not be perfect.]

Denote the open rectangle by R_-. Then (i) RP is closed, (ii) RP contains $R_- P$, which is evidently **D**. H(RP) is not null.

Prop. 19. *A perfect set* P *has cardinal* c.

If the set is unbounded let p be a point of P, R a rectangle about p. RP contains a bounded perfect set by the Lemma, and it is enough to consider *bounded* P.

Lemma. A bounded closed non-null linear set has a "first" and a "last" point.

Let a be a point to the left of the set, p to the right of a. For some p the interval (ap) contains no point of the set, for others (ap) contains such points. Let q be the dividing point in the Dedekind section. Evidently q has a point of the set in an arbitrary neighbourhood; q must be a point of the set, and is evidently the first point.

Cor. Given any bounded closed set E *and a straight line* L. *If the line has points common with* E *it has a "first" intersection.*

For LE is a bounded closed linear set.

Proof of Prop. 19 *for bounded sets.*

The proof is an induction from n to $(n + 1)$ dimensions. For simplicity we take the case 2 to 3.

Consider S, the set of projections on $z = 0$. This is closed, since, if l is a limit point, the ordinate L (parallel to Oz) at l is distant 0 from P, therefore (since L and P are closed) has points common with P (Prop. 5, Cor. 2), so that l belongs to S.

(i) If S is not perfect it has isolated points p. The z-ordinate at p contains a set E contained in P, and this E is closed; and perfect, since an isolated point of E would evidently be an isolated point of P. P contains a linear perfect set, therefore contains c points.

(ii) Suppose then S is perfect. In this case we associate with every p of S the *lowest* q of P that has p as projection. The set of q's is similar to the set of p's, which is a perfect set in "n" dimensions, and therefore has cardinal c by hypothesis.

Cor. 1. *In any (rectangular) neighbourhood* R *of a point of a perfect set* P *there are c points of the set. In particular every point of* P *is a point of condensation.*

For, by the lemma, RP contains a perfect set.

Cor. 2. *In any dissection of a closed set into a perfect set* P *and a denumerable set* D, P *is the set of points of condensation. In particular the dissection is unique.*

By Cor. 1 a point of P is a point of condensation; we have, therefore, only to show that a point q of D is *not* a point of condensation, i.e. is contained in a rectangle containing only a denumerable set of points of E. But q is at non-zero distance δ from P; therefore a sphere about q with radius $< \delta$ contains only a sub-class of D, and so only a denumerable set of points of E.

Cor. 3. *A closed set has cardinal c or* Ξ_0, *or is finite.*

Cor. 4. *A denumerable closed set is denumerable in a determinate way.*

For the perfect component is absent, and the set is a C.

DOVER BOOKS ON SCIENCE

Abbott, Edwin A. FLATLAND. Introduction by Banesh Hoffman. 128pp. 5⅜ x 8.

Clothbound $2.50
Paperbound $1.00

Abro, A. d'. THE EVOLUTION OF SCIENTIFIC THOUGHT: FROM NEWTON TO EINSTEIN. Second revised and enlarged edition. 21 diagrams. 15 portraits. xx + 481pp. 5⅜ x 8.
Clothbound $3.95

Abro, A. d'. THE RISE OF THE NEW PHYSICS. Second revised edition. Two volume set. 994pp. 5⅜ x 8. 38 portraits.
The Set: **Paperbound $3.90**

Adams, F. D. THE BIRTH AND DEVELOPMENT OF THE GEOLOGICAL SCIENCES. 79 illustrations. 15 full page plates. v + 506pp. 5⅜ x 8.

Clothbound $3.95
Paperbound $1.95

Agricola, Georgius. DE RE METALLICA. Translated by Herbert Hoover and Lou Henry Hoover. 3 indexes. 289 illus. xxxi + 638pp. 6¾ x 10¾. **Clothbound $10.00**

Archimedes. WORKS (including 'The Method of Archimedes). Edited by T. L. Heath. 506pp. 5⅜ x 8. **Clothbound $4.95**
Paperbound $1.95

Ayer, Alfred Jules. LANGUAGE, TRUTH AND LOGIC. Second revised edition. Index. 160pp. 5⅜ x 8. **Clothbound $2.50**
Paperbound $1.25

Bartram, William, TRAVELS. Unabridged. Introduction by Mark Van Doren. 413pp. 5⅜ x 8.

Clothbound $3.95
Paperbound $1.90

Bateman, H. PARTIAL DIFFERENTIAL EQUATIONS OF MATHE-
MATICAL PHYSICS. Index. 29 ill. xxii + 522pp. 6 x 9.
Clothbound $4.95

Blaschke, Wilhelm. VORLESUNGEN UBER DIFFERENTIAL
GEOMETRIE, Vol. I: Elementare Differential Geometrie. Third
revised edition. German text. 35 figures. xiv + 322pp.
5½ x 8½. **Clothbound $3.95**

Bonola, Robert. NON-EUCLIDEAN GEOMETRY. Authorized
English translation with additional appendices by H. S.
Carslaw and an introduction by Federigo Enriques. This
new edition contains an appendix of the G. B. Halsted
translations of Lobachevski's "The Theory of Parallels" and
Bolyai's "The Science of Absolute Space." 431pp. 5⅜ x 8.
Clothbound $3.95
Paperbound $1.90

Boole, George. LAWS OF THOUGHT. 448pp. 5⅜ x 8.
Clothbound $4.50
Paperbound $1.90

Born, Max. THE RESTLESS UNIVERSE. Second revised edition.
120 drawings and figures. 12 plates. 3 tables. 315pp.
6⅛ x 9¼. **Clothbound $3.95**

Bragg, William. CONCERNING THE NATURE OF THINGS.
57 figures. 32 plates. 264pp. 5⅜ x 8. **Clothbound $2.75**
Paperbound $1.25

Bridgman, P. W. THE NATURE OF PHYSICAL THEORY. Index.
xi + 138pp. 5⅜ x 8. **Clothbound $2.50**
Paperbound $1.25

Brillouin, Léon. WAVE PROPAGATION IN PERIODIC STRUC-
TURES. Second revised edition. Index. xii + 259pp.
5⅜ x 8. **Clothbound $3.75**
Paperbound $1.85

Campbell, Norman. WHAT IS SCIENCE? Index. 186pp.
5⅜ x 8.
Paperbound $1.25

Cantor, Georg. CONTRIBUTIONS TO THE FOUNDING OF THE THEORY OF TRANSFINITE NUMBERS. Translated from German and with introduction and notes by Philip E. B. Jourdain. Bibliog. Index. ix + 211pp. 5⅜ x 8.

Clothbound $2.75
Paperbound $1.25

Carslaw, H. S. INTRODUCTION TO THE THEORY OF FOURIER'S SERIES AND INTEGRALS. Third revised edition. Index. 39 ill. xiii + 368pp. 5⅜ x 8.   **Clothbound $4.50**
Paperbound $1.95

Cassirer, Ernst. SUBSTANCE AND FUNCTION AND EINSTEIN'S THEORY OF RELATIVITY. Two books bound as one. Bibliog. Index. 465pp. 5⅜ x 8.   **Clothbound $3.95**
Paperbound $1.95

Davis, William Morris. GEOGRAPHICAL ESSAYS. Edited by D. W. Johnson. Index. 784pp. 5⅜ x 8.   **Clothbound $5.50**

Debye, P. POLAR MOLECULES. Index. 33 ill. iv + 172pp. 5⅜ x 8   **Clothbound $3.50**
Paperbound $1.50

Deimel, Richard F. MECHANICS OF THE GYROSCOPE: Dynamics of Rotation. 75 diagrams. 208pp. 5⅜ x 8.

Clothbound $3.50
Paperbound $1.60

De Morgan, Augustus. A BUDGET OF PARADOXES. Unabridged republication of the second edition, edited by D. E. Smith. New introduction by Prof. Ernest Nagel, Columbia University. Two volumes bound as one. Vol. I: viii + 407pp. Vol. II 387pp. 5⅜ x 8.

Clothbound $4.95

Descartes, René. THE GEOMETRY. The complete French text in facsimile plus the complete translation by D. E. Smith and M. L. Latham vii + 246pp. 5⅜ x 8.

Clothbound $2.95
Paperbound $1.50

Dewey, John. ESSAYS IN EXPERIMENTAL LOGIC. vii + 444pp. 5⅜ x 8.   **Clothbound $3.50**
Paperbound $1.75

Dreyer, J. L. E. A HISTORY OF ASTRONOMY FROM THALES TO KEPLER. (Formerly titled 'History of Planetary Systems from Thales to Kepler.') 448pp. 5⅜ x 8.

Paperbound $1.95

Einstein, Lorentz, Minkowski, and Weyl. THE PRINCIPLE OF RELATIVITY. An English translation of eleven of the most important original papers on the general and special theories of relativity. Notes by Sommerfeld. Trans. by Perrett and Jeffrey. viii + 216pp. 5⅜ x 8.

Clothbound $3.50
Paperbound $1.50

Emmons, Howard W. GAS DYNAMICS TABLES FOR AIR. 3 ill. 10 graphs. 4 tables. 46pp. 6⅛ x 9¼.

Paperbound $1.75

Enciso, Jorge. DESIGN MOTIFS OF ANCIENT MEXICO. 155 plates. 192pp. 7⅞ x 10¾. **Clothbound $3.95**

Euclid. THE ELEMENTS. Heath edition. Vol. I: 448pp. Vol. II: 448pp. Vol. III: 560pp.

The Set: Paperbound $5.85

Findlay, Alexander. THE PHASE RULE AND ITS APPLICATIONS. New, revised, enlarged edition brought up to date by Campbell and Smith. Index. 235 diagrams. xii + 500pp. 5⅜ x 8. **Clothbound $5.00**
Paperbound $1.90

Fry, William J., Taylor, John M., and Henvis, Bertha W. DESIGN OF CRYSTAL VIBRATING SYSTEMS. Second revised edition. 126 graphs. viii + 182pp. 6⅛ x 9¼

Clothbound $3.50

Galilei, Galileo. DIALOGUES CONCERNING TWO NEW SCIENCES. Trans. by Henry Crew and Alfonso De Salvio. Intro. by Antonio Favaro. Bibliog. Index. 126 diagrams. xxi + 300pp. 5⅜ x 8. **Clothbound $3.50**
Paperbound $1.50

Gutenberg, Beno. INTERNAL CONSTITUTION OF THE EARTH. Second revised edition. Bibliog. 1098 references. 43 diagrams, photographs, and graphs. 88 tables. 439pp. 6⅛ x 9¼.
Clothbound $5.50

Hadamard, Jacques. LECTURES ON CAUCHY'S PROBLEM IN LINEAR PARTIAL DIFFERENTIAL EQUATIONS. Index. v + 316pp. 5⅜ x 8.
Paperbound $1.70

Hadamard, Jacques. THE PSYCHOLOGY OF INVENTION IN THE MATHEMATICAL FIELD. xiii + 145pp. 5⅜ x 8.
Clothbound $2.50
Paperbound $1.25

Hay, G. E. VECTOR AND TENSOR ANALYSIS. 208pp. 5⅜ x 8.
Clothbound $2.75
Paperbound $1.60

Heaviside, Oliver. ELECTROMAGNETIC THEORY. Biographical introduction by Ernst Weber. Unabridged one-volume edition of the three-volume work. Bibliog. xxx + 386pp. 8 x 12¼.
Clothbound $7.50

Heisenberg, Werner. THE PHYSICAL PRINCIPLES OF THE QUANTUM THEORY. Trans. by Eckart and Hoyt. Index. viii 184pp. 5⅜ x 8.
Clothbound $2.75
Paperbound $1.25

Helmholtz, Hermann L. F. SENSATIONS OF TONE. Unabridged reissue of the last English edition, with a new introduction by Henry Margenau. Index. 608pp. 6⅛ x 9¼.
Clothbound $4.95

Hertz, Heinrich. PRINCIPLES OF MECHANICS. New introduction by Robert S. Cohen, Wesleyan University. 5⅜ x 8.
Clothbound $3.50
Paperbound $1.75

Herzberg, Gerhard. ATOMIC SPECTRA AND ATOMIC STRUCTURE. Trans. by J. W. T. Spinks. Second revised edition. Index. 80 ill. 21 tables. xv + 257pp. 5¼ x 8¼.
Clothbound $3.95
Paperbound $1.90

Hopf, L. INTRODUCTION TO THE DIFFERENTIAL EQUATIONS OF PHYSICS. Trans. by Walter Nef. Index. 48 ill. vi + 154pp. 4¼ x 6⅜. **Clothbound $2.50**
Paperbound $1.25

Ince, E. L. ORDINARY DIFFERENTIAL EQUATIONS. Fourth revised edition. Index. 18 ill. viii + 558pp. 5½ x 9.
Clothbound $4.95

Jahnke, Eugene and **Emde, Fritz.** TABLES OF FUNCTIONS WITH FORMULAE AND CURVES. (Funktionentafeln). Fourth revised edition. Text in German and English. Index. 212 ill. xv + 382pp. 5½ x 8½. **Paperbound $1.90**

Jeans, James. THE DYNAMICAL THEORY OF GASES. Republication of the third revised edition. 444pp. 5⅜ x 8.
Clothbound $3.95
Paperbound $2.00

Jessop, H. T. and **Harris F. C.** PHOTOELASTICITY: PRINCIPLES AND METHODS. Index. 164 diagrams. vii + 184pp. 6⅛ x 9¼. **Clothbound $3.75**

Kamke, E. THEORY OF SETS. Trans. by F. Bagemihl from second German edition. Bibliog. Index. vii + 152pp. 5⅜ x 8.
Clothbound $2.75
Paperbound $1.25

Kellogg, Oliver Dimon. FOUNDATIONS OF POTENTIAL THEORY. Index. ix + 384pp. 5⅜ x 8. **Clothbound $3.95**
Paperbound $1.90

Khinchin, A. I. MATHEMATICAL FOUNDATIONS OF STATISTICAL MECHANICS. Trans. by G. Gamow. Index viii + 179pp. 5 x 7⅜. **Clothbound $2.95**
Paperbound $1.35

Klein, Felix. ELEMENTARY MATHEMATICS FROM AN ADVANCED STANDPOINT. Vol. I: Arithmetic, Algebra, Analysis. Translated from the third German edition by E. R. Hedrick and C. A. Noble. Index. 125 ill. xiv + 274pp. 5⅜ x 8. **Paperbound $1.60**

Klein, Felix. ELEMENTARY MATHEMATICS from an Advanced Standpoint. Vol. II: Geometry translated from the third German edition by E. A. Hedrick and C. A. Noble. Index. 141 ill. ix + 214pp. 5⅜ x 8.

Paperbound $1.60

Knopp, Konrad. ELEMENTS OF THE THEORY OF FUNCTIONS. Trans. by Frederick Bagemihl. Bibliog. Index. 160pp. 5⅜ x 8.

Clothbound $2.50
Paperbound $1.25

Knopp, Konrad. THEORY OF FUNCTIONS, Part I. Trans. from the fifth German edition by Frederick Bagemihl. Bibliog. Index. 4 ill. xii + 146pp. 5⅜ x 8. **Clothbound $2.50**
Paperbound $1.25

Knopp, Konrad. THEORY OF FUNCTIONS, Part II. Trans. by Frederick Bagemihl. Bibliog. 7 ill. x + 150pp. 5⅜ x 8.

Clothbound $2.50
Paperbound $1.25

Knopp, Konrad. PROBLEM BOOK IN THE THEORY OF FUNCTIONS. Vol. I: Problems in the Elementary Theory of Functions. Trans. by Lipman Bers. viii + 126pp. 5⅜ x 8.

Clothbound $2.50
Paperbound $1.25

Knopp, Konrad. PROBLEM BOOK IN THE THEORY OF FUNCTIONS. Vol. II: Problems in the Advanced Theory of Functions. Trans. by Frederick Bagemihl. 144pp. 5⅜ x 8.

Clothbound $2.50
Paperbound $1.25

Kober, H. DICTIONARY OF CONFORMAL REPRESENTATIONS. 447 diagrams. xvi + 208pp. 6⅛ x 9¼.

Clothbound $3.95

Kraitchik, Maurice. MATHEMATICAL RECREATIONS. Second revised edition. 181 ill. Over 40 tables. 328pp. 5⅜ x 8.

Clothbound $3.50
Paperbound $1.60

Lamb, Horace. HYDRODYNAMICS. Sixth revised edition. 83 ill. xviii + 738pp. 6 x 9. **Clothbound $5.95**

Langer, Susanne K. AN INTRODUCTION TO SYMBOLIC LOGIC. Second revised edition corrected and expanded. 368pp. 5⅜ x 8. **Clothbound $3.50**
Paperbound $1.60

Laplace, Pierre Simon. A PHILOSOPHICAL ESSAY ON PROBABILITIES. Trans. by Truscott and Emory. Intro. by E. T. Bell. viii + 196pp. 5⅜ x 8¼. **Clothbound $2.75**
Paperbound $1.25

Lewis, Clarence Irving, and **Langford, Cooper Harold.** SYMBOLIC LOGIC. Index. 8 diagrams. vii + 504pp. 5⅜ x 8. **Clothbound $4.50**

Littlewood, J. E. ELEMENTS OF THE THEORY OF REAL FUNCTIONS. 5⅜ x 8. **Clothbound $2.85**
Paperbound $1.35

Lorentz, H. A. THE THEORY OF ELECTRONS AND ITS APPLICATIONS TO THE PHENOMENA OF LIGHT AND RADIANT HEAT. Unabridged, unaltered reissue of the second edition. Index. 9 figures. Appendix. 352pp. 5⅜ x 8. **Clothbound $3.50**
Paperbound $1.70

Lotka, Alfred J. ELEMENTS OF PHYSICAL BIOLOGY. With a new introduction by Dr. Lowell Reed. Bibliog. Index. xxx + 460pp. 5⅜ x 8. **Clothbound $3.95**
Paperbound $1.95

Love, A. E. H. A TREATISE ON THE MATHEMATICAL THEORY OF ELASTICITY. Fourth revised edition. Index. 76 ill. xxi + 643pp. 6 x 9. **Clothbound $5.95**

Lovitt, William Vernon. LINEAR INTEGRAL EQUATIONS. Index. 27 diagrams. xii + 253pp. 5⅜ x 8. **Clothbound $3.50**

Mach, Ernst. PRINCIPLES OF PHYSICAL OPTICS. Unabridged reissue of the English translation of the last German edition. 10 plates. 280 diagrams. x + 324pp. 5⅜ x 8. **Clothbound $3.50**
Paperbound $1.75

MacRobert, T. M. SPHERICAL HARMONICS. An Elementary Treatise on Harmonic Functions with Applications. Second revised edition. Index. 20 diagrams. vi + 372pp. 5½ x 8½.
Clothbound $4.50

Mann, H. B. ANALYSIS AND DESIGN OF EXPERIMENTS. Analysis of Variance and Analysis of Variance Designs. Index. 3 tables. vi + 195pp. 5 x 7⅜.
Paperbound $1.25

Mason, Max and **Weaver, Warren.** THE ELECTROMAGNETIC FIELD. Index. 61 diagrams. xiii + 396pp. 5⅜ x 8.
Clothbound $3.95
Paperbound $1.90

Maxwell, James Clerk. ELECTRICITY AND MAGNETISM. An unabridged republication of the third edition. Two volumes bound as one. Vol. I: xxxii + 506pp. Vol. II: xxiv 500pp. 5⅜ x 8.
Clothbound $4.95

Maxwell, James Clerk. MATTER AND MOTION. Notes by Sir Joseph Larmor. Index. 17 diagrams. 178pp. 5¾ x 8¼.
Clothbound $2.75
Paperbound $1.25

Maxwell, James Clerk. SCIENTIFIC PAPERS. Complete and unabridged. Two volumes bound as one. 1488pp. 5⅜ x 8.
Clothbound $10.00

McLachlan, N. W. THEORY OF VIBRATIONS. Index. 99 diagrams. vi + 154pp. 5 x 7⅜.   **Clothbound $2.50**
Paperbound $1.35

Meinzer, Oscar E. HYDROLOGY. Physics of the Earth Series. Bibliog. Index. 165 ill. 23 tables. xi + 712pp. 6⅛ x 9¼.
Clothbound $4.95

Mellor, J. W. HIGHER MATHEMATICS FOR STUDENTS OF CHEMISTRY AND PHYSICS. Fourth revised edition. Index. 189 figures. 18 tables. xxix + 641pp. 5½ x 8⅛.
Clothbound $3.95
Paperbound $2.00

Milne-Thompson, L. M. JACOBIAN ELLIPTIC FUNCTION TABLES. xi + 123pp. 5 x 7⅜.   **Clothbound $2.45**

Minnaert, M. THE NATURE OF LIGHT AND COLOUR IN THE OPEN AIR. Trans. by H. M. Kremer-Priest and K. E. Brian Jay. Index. 202 ill. including 42 photographs. xvi + 362pp. 5⅜ x 8.

Paperbound $1.95

Mott-Smith, Geoffrey. MATHEMATICAL PUZZLES FOR BEGINNERS AND ENTHUSIASTS. Second revised edition. 256pp. 5⅜ x 8.

Clothbound $2.25
Paperbound $1.00

Newton, Isaac. OPTICKS. Preface by Professor I. B. Cohen. Foreword by Professor Albert Einstein. Intro. by E. T. Whittaker. cxv + 406pp. 4½ x 7.

Paperbound $1.90

Norris, P. W. and **Legge, W. Seymour.** MECHANICS VIA THE CALCULUS. Third revised edition. 195 diagrams. xii + 372pp. 5½ x 8¼.

Clothbound $3.95

Oparin, A. I. THE ORIGIN OF LIFE. New introduction by Dr. S. Morgulis. xxv + 270pp. 5⅜ x 8.

Paperbound $1.70

Planck, Max. TREATISE ON THERMODYNAMICS. Trans. by Alexander Ogg. Third revised edition. Trans. from the seventh German edition. Index. 5 ill. xxxii + 297pp. 5⅜ x 8.

Clothbound $3.50
Paperbound $1.75

Poincaré, Henri. SCIENCE AND HYPOTHESIS. Index. xxvii + 244pp. 5⅜ x 8.

Clothbound $2.50
Paperbound $1.25

Poincaré, Henri. SCIENCE AND METHOD. Trans. by Francis Maitland. 288pp. 5⅜ x 8.

Clothbound $2.50
Paperbound $1.25